OCR Functional Skills

Mathematics Pilot

WITHDRAWN

Greg Byrd   Lynn Byrd

OCR
RECOGNISING ACHIEVEMENT

Heinemann

Official Publisher Partnership

OCR AND HEINEMANN WORKING TOGETHER TO PROVIDE BETTER SUPPORT FOR YOU

Heinemann is an imprint of Pearson Education Limited, a company incorporated in England and Wales, having its registered office at Edinburgh Gate, Harlow, Essex, CM20 2JE. Registered company number: 872828

www.heinemann.co.uk

Heinemann is a registered trademark of Pearson Education Ltd

Text © Pearson Education Limited 2009

First published 2009

13 12 11 10 09
10 9 8 7 6 5 4 3 2 1

British Library Cataloguing in Publication Data

A catalogue record for this book is available from the British Library

ISBN 978 0 435502 60 7

Edited by Saskia Besier

Designed by Jordan Publishing Design, Salisbury

Typeset by Jordan Publishing Design, Salisbury

Original illustrations © Pearson Education Ltd, 2009

Illustrated by Nigel Jordan

Cover design by Christopher Howson and Pete Stratton

Picture research by Chrissie Martin

Cover photo/illustration © iStock Photo/Sabrina del Nabili

Printed in Italy by Rotolito

Acknowledgements

The author and publisher would like to thank the following individuals and organisations for permission to reproduce photographs:

Pearson Education / Debbie Rowe p2; Pearson Education / Jules Selmes p4; PhotoDisc p5; Alamy / Barry Mason p6; PhotoDisc p8; Pearson Education / Malcolm Harris p10 (eggs); Pearson Education / Ian Wedgewood p10 (background); Pearson Education / Tudor Photography p11; iStockPhoto / Leigh Schindler p12; Pearson Education / Rob Judges p13 (chef); Alamy / Mark Hodson Stock Photography p13 (food); Shutterstock / Elena Elisseeva p14; Shutterstock / Vasyl Helevachuk p15; Getty Images / PhotoDisc p16 (background); Brand X Pictures p16 (jam jars); Shutterstock / Vonkara p16 (van); PhotoDisc p18 (background); Pearson Education / Tudor Photography (lamb); Michelin p20 & p52 (background); Pearson Education / Martin Sookias p21; PhotoDisc p22 (background); Pearson Education / Tudor Photography p22 (sleeping bag); Alamy / Nature PL p23; Shutterstock / J Freeman p24; Corbis / Stockbyte p40; Brand X Pictures p42; PhotoDisc p43; Shutterstock Factoria singular fotografia p44; Getty Images / Matthew Ward p45 (kitchen cupboard); Pearson Education / Rob Judges p45 (chef); Shutterstock / Rui Manuel Teles Gomes p46; PhotoDisc p48 (background); Shutterstock / adv p48 (pots); PhotoDisc p50; Shutterstock / Samot p54; PhotoDisc p56 (background); Pearson Education / Tudor Photography p56 (camping equipment)

Every effort has been made to contact copyright holders of material reproduced in this book. Any omissions will be rectified in subsequent printings if notice is given to the publishers.

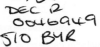

Contents

Introduction

Welcome to the OCR Functional Maths Pilot!

This book covers Level 1 and Level 2 Maths for the OCR Functional Maths Pilot. Using a highly visual approach, the book aims to motivate students to develop the skills they need to pass the OCR Functional Maths Pilot, and to use maths more effectively in their daily lives. Many of the Level 1 tasks are further developed at Level 2, so there are lots of opportunities to practise and improve.

Here are some of the main features of this book…

Introducing Process Skills

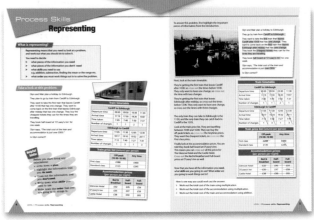

These sections guide you through the Process Skills: Representing, Analysing and Interpreting. They will show you what each skill means and how they can help you solve real world problems.

Level Introduction

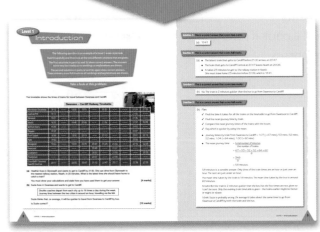

These sections show you examples of an exam-style task, and what both basic and excellent answers look like. This book is designed to help you produce excellent answers!

Highly visual practice tasks

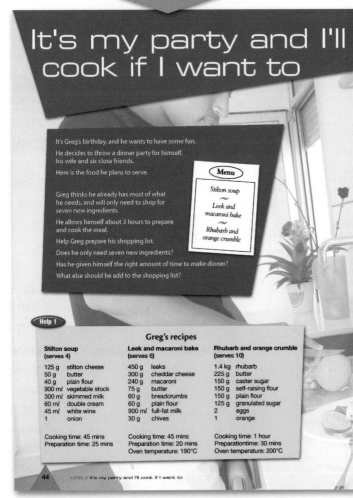

The information you need is provided in handy panels. Be careful though, not all of the information is relevant. That's part of the task – deciding what information is and isn't going to help you solve the problem.

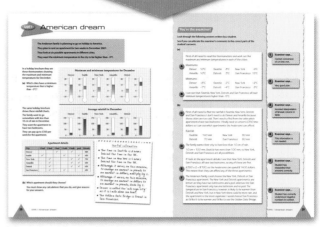

Highly visual practice tasks are set in real-life situations, so it's easy to see why the maths is useful.

These sections give you even more tasks to practise. They include a student's sample answer, together with examiner's comments for you to try to match up. See if you can understand where the student is gaining or losing marks.

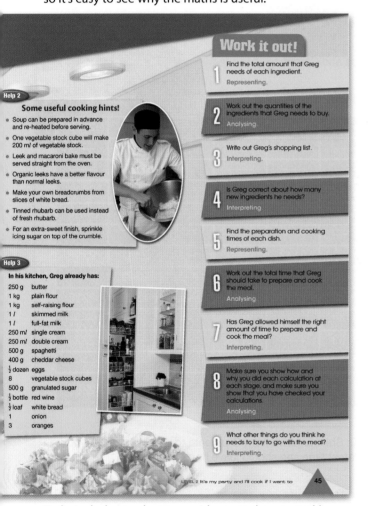

Tasks include step by step guidance on how to tackle the problems. As you practise and progress to later tasks, there is less and less guidance, until you can tackle the task successfully alone.

Further practice tasks

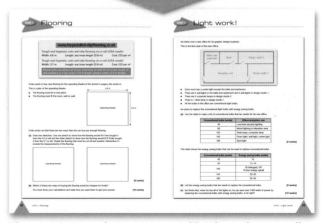

These practice tasks appear more like the tasks you will meet in the exam. Each section shows how many marks are allocated. See if you can use all that you have learned to develop top-mark answers.

Introduction

The following question is an example of a Level 1 exam-style task.

Read it carefully and then look at the two different solutions that are given.

The first solutions in parts (a) and (b) show correct answers. The answers score very low marks as no workings or explanations are shown.

The second solutions in parts (a) and (b) again show correct answers. These answers score full marks as all workings and explanations are shown.

Take a look at this problem:

The timetable shows the times of trains for travel between Swansea and Cardiff.

Swansea – Cardiff Railway Timetable

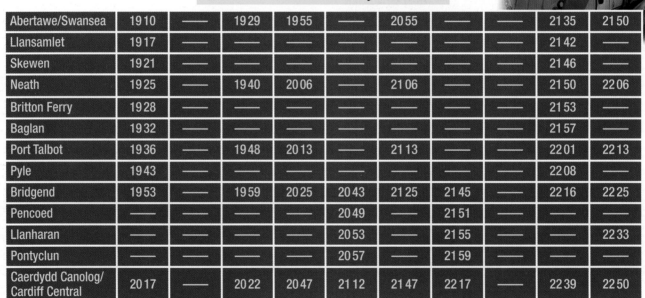

Abertawe/Swansea	1910	—	1929	1955	—	2055	—	—	2135	2150
Llansamlet	1917	—	—	—	—	—	—	—	2142	—
Skewen	1921	—	—	—	—	—	—	—	2146	—
Neath	1925	—	1940	2006	—	2106	—	—	2150	2206
Britton Ferry	1928	—	—	—	—	—	—	—	2153	—
Baglan	1932	—	—	—	—	—	—	—	2157	—
Port Talbot	1936	—	1948	2013	—	2113	—	—	2201	2213
Pyle	1943	—	—	—	—	—	—	—	2208	—
Bridgend	1953	—	1959	2025	2043	2125	2145	—	2216	2225
Pencoed	—	—	—	—	2049	—	2151	—	—	—
Llanharan	—	—	—	—	2053	—	2155	—	—	2233
Pontyclun	—	—	—	—	2057	—	2159	—	—	—
Caerdydd Canolog/ Cardiff Central	2017	—	2022	2047	2112	2147	2217	—	2239	2250

(a) Heather lives in Glynneath and wants to get to Cardiff by 2100. She can drive from Glynneath to the nearest railway station, Neath, in 25 minutes. What is the latest time she should leave home to catch a train?

You must show your calculations and state how you have used them to get your answer. **[4 marks]**

(b) Suzie lives in Swansea and wants to get to Cardiff.

> Shuttle coaches depart from each city up to 16 times a day during the week. Journey time between the two cities is around an hour, travelling via the M4.

Suzie thinks that, on average, it will be quicker to travel from Swansea to Cardiff by bus.

Is Suzie correct? **[12 marks]**

Solution 1: This is a correct answer that scores **two** marks:

(a)   1941

Solution 2: This is a correct answer that scores **full** marks:

(a)
● The latest train that gets to Cardiff before 21 00 arrives at 20 47.

● The train that gets to Cardiff Central at 20 47 leaves Neath at 20 06.

● It takes 25 minutes to get to the railway station in Neath.
  She must leave home 25 minutes before 20 06, which is 19 41.

Solution 1: This is a correct answer that scores **two** marks:

(b)   No. The train is 2 minutes quicker than the bus to go from Swansea to Cardiff.

Solution 2: This is a correct answer that scores **full** marks:

(b)   Plan:
✓ Find the time it takes for all the trains on the timetable to go from Swansea to Cardiff.

✓ Find the mean journey time by train.

✓ Compare the mean journey times of the trains with the buses.

✓ Say which is quicker by using the mean.

● Journey times by train from Swansea to Cardiff = 1:07 (= 67 mins), 53 mins, 52 mins, 52 mins, 1:04 (= 64 mins), 1:00 (= 60 mins)

● The mean journey time

$$= \frac{\text{total number of minutes}}{\text{the number of trains}}$$

$$= \frac{67 + 53 + 52 + 52 + 64 + 60}{6}$$

$$= \frac{348}{6}$$

$$= 58 \text{ minutes.}$$

58 minutes is a sensible answer. Only three of the train times are an hour or just over an hour. The rest are just under an hour.

The mean time taken by the train is 58 minutes. The mean time taken by the bus is around 60 minutes.

It looks like the train is 2 minutes quicker than the bus, but the bus times are not given so I can't be sure. Only the evening train timetable is given – the trains earlier might be faster or might be slower.

I think Suzie is probably wrong. On average it takes about the same time to go from Swansea to Cardiff by both the train and the bus.

Representing

What is representing?

Representing means that you need to look at a problem, and work out what you should do to solve it.

You need to decide

▶ what pieces of the information you **need**

▶ what pieces of the information you **don't need**

▶ what **skills** you need to use
e.g. addition, subtraction, finding the mean or the range etc.

▶ what **order** you must work things out in to solve the problem.

Take a look at this problem:

Glyn and Mair plan a holiday to Edinburgh.

They plan to go by train from Cardiff to Edinburgh.

They want to take the first train that leaves Cardiff after 10 00 that has one change. They want to come back on the first train that leaves Edinburgh after midday that has one change. They buy the cheapest tickets they can for the times they are travelling.

They book half-board at 'O'Leary's Inn' for one week.

Glyn says, *"The total cost of the train and accommodation is just over £800."*

Is Glyn correct?

Helpful hints:

Before you start doing any calculations:

● write down a **plan**.

● highlight the information that you **do need**.

● Cross out the information that you **don't need**.

● Write down what **skills** you need to use.

● Write down the **order** that you are going to do things in.

Train timetable

Cardiff to Edinburgh				
Departure time	09 30	09 50	10 30	11 30
Arrival time	17 19	17 30	18 20	19 07
Time taken	7:49	7:40	7:50	7:37
Number of changes	1	1	2	1
Edinburgh to Cardiff				
Departure time	11 05	11 30	12 05	12 30
Arrival time	18 17	19 10	19 32	20 11
Time taken	7:12	7:40	7:27	7:41
Number of changes	1	3	1	3

Train price list (return) per person

	Off-peak (10 00–16 00)	Any time
First class	£288	£490
Standard class	£135	£245

Accommodation prices (per person per night)

	Bed & Breakfast	Half-board	Full-board
Glencoe Hotel	£32	£45	£54
O'Leary's Inn	£35	£47	£59
Castle Hotel	£38	£50	£65

To answer this problem, first highlight the important pieces of information from the introduction.

Glyn and Mair plan a holiday to Edinburgh.

They go by train from Cardiff to Edinburgh.

They want to take the first train that leaves Cardiff after 10 00 that has one change. They want to come back on the first train that leaves Edinburgh after midday that has one change. They book the cheapest tickets they can for the times they are travelling.

They book half-board at 'O'Leary's Inn' for one week.

Glyn says, *"The total cost of the train and accommodation is just over £800."*

Is Glyn correct?

Next, look at the train timetable.

They're getting the first train that leaves Cardiff after 10 00, so cross out the times before 10 00. They only want to have one change, so cross out the time with two changes.

They're getting the first train that leaves Edinburgh after midday, so cross out the times before 12 00. They only want to have one change, so cross out the times with three changes.

The only train they can take to Edinburgh is the 11 30, and the only train they can catch back to Cardiff is the 12 05.

Look at the train price list. They are travelling between 10 00 and 16 00. They can buy the off-peak tickets, so cross out the Anytime prices. They want the cheapest tickets, so cross out the First class price.

Finally look at the accommodation prices. You are told they book half-board at O'Leary's Inn. This means you can cross out all the prices for The Glencoe Hotel and the Castle Hotel. Cross out the Bed & Breakfast and Full-board prices at O'Leary's Inn as well.

Now that you have all the information you **need**, what **skills** are you going to use? What **order** are you going to work things out in?

Train timetable

Cardiff to Edinburgh

Departure time	09 30	09 50	10 30	11 30
Arrival time	17 19	17 30	18 20	19 07
Time taken	7:49	7:40	7:50	7:37
Number of changes	1	1	2	1

Edinburgh to Cardiff

Departure time	11 05	11 30	12 05	12 30
Arrival time	18 17	19 10	19 32	20 11
Time taken	7:12	7:40	7:27	7:41
Number of changes	1	3	1	3

Train price list (return) per person

	Off-peak (10 00–16 00)	Any time
First class	£288	£490
Standard class	£135	£245

Accommodation prices (per person per night)

	Bed & Breakfast	Half-board	Full-board
Glencoe Hotel	£32	£45	£54
O'Leary's Inn	£35	£47	£59
Castle Hotel	£38	£50	£65

Here is one way you could work out the answer:
- Work out the total cost of the train using multiplication.
- Work out the total cost of the accommodation using multiplication.
- Work out the total cost of the train and accommodation using addition.

Analysing

What is analysing?

Analysing means that you need to use the skills you wrote down in your **representing** plan, and work out the answers.

You need to

▶ **be organised** and follow your plan

▶ use mathematical skills to **work out** answers

▶ **check** your calculations to make sure the answers make sense

▶ **write down** all the calculations that you do and explain why you are doing them.

Take a look at this problem:

Let's continue with Glyn and Mair's holiday to Edinburgh. This is a reminder of the key points.

Glyn and Mair plan a holiday to Edinburgh.

They plan to go by train from Cardiff to Edinburgh.

They want to take the first train that leaves Cardiff after 10 00 that has one change. They want to come back on the first train that leaves Edinburgh after mid-day that has one change. They buy the cheapest tickets they can for the times they are travelling.

They book half-board at 'O'Leary's Inn' for one week.

Glyn says, *"The total cost of the train and accommodation is just over £800."*

Is Glyn correct?

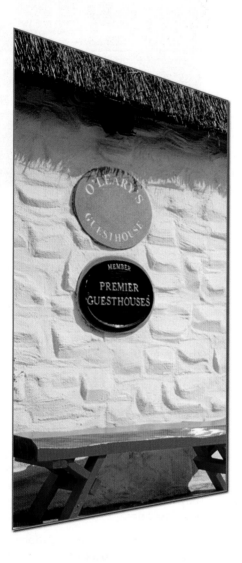

From the **representing** section, this was a plan you could follow.

▶ Work out the total cost of the train using multiplication.

▶ Work out the total cost of the accommodation using multiplication.

▶ Work out the total cost of the train and accommodation using addition.

Helpful hints:

Follow your plan and

● **organise** your work so that you can follow it and so that other people can follow it too

● **write down** what you are finding at every stage

● **work out** your answers accurately

● **check** your calculations at every stage

● **write down** all the calculations that you do

● **write down** all the checks that you do

● don't worry if you have to change your plan part way through the problem – just make sure you **write down** what you have changed and why you have changed it.

Step 1

Work out the total cost of the train using multiplication.

To do this you use the train price list.

You should notice that these prices are for the return trip and they are per person.

	Off-peak (1000–1600)	Anytime
First class	~~£288~~	£490
Standard class	£135	£245

So, to find the total price, you need to multiply by 2

$£135 \times 2 = \underline{\mathbf{£270}}$ ✓

Check by estimating

$£140 \times 2 = \underline{\mathbf{£280}}$

Step 2

Work out the total cost of the accommodation using multiplication.

Remember that these prices are per night per person.

Also remember that Glyn and Mair are staying for one week (seven nights).

	Bed & Breakfast	Half board	Full board
Glencoe Hotel	~~£32~~	£45	£54
O'Leary's Inn	~~£35~~	£47	~~£59~~
Castle Hotel	~~£38~~	£50	~~£65~~

So for one night for Glyn and Mair it would cost

$£47 \times 2 = £94$

So for seven nights for Glyn and Mair it would cost

$£94 \times 7 = \underline{\mathbf{£658}}$ ✓

Check by estimating

$£50 \times 2 = £100$

$£100 \times 7 = \underline{\mathbf{£700}}$

Step 3

Work out the total cost of the train and accommodation using addition.

The train costs £270, the accommodation costs £658.

So the total is

$£270 + £658 = \underline{\mathbf{£928}}$ ✓

Check by estimating

$£300 + £700 = \underline{\mathbf{£1000}}$

The plan you have used to work out the final total isn't the *only* plan possible.

> You could have followed this plan instead.
> ▶ Work out the total cost of the accommodation using multiplication.
> ▶ Work out the total cost of the train using multiplication.
> ▶ Work out the total cost of the train and accommodation using addition.

It doesn't matter whether you work out the accommodation or the train costs first.
As long as you do both, you can work out the total cost. You can do them in whatever order you like.

You have found the total cost of the train and accommodation. You are now ready to move on to the final stage of **interpreting** your answer.

Interpreting

What is interpreting?

Interpreting means that you need to be able to use the answers to the calculations you have done. You need to explain what the answers mean, and how they relate to the problem.

You need to

▶ **explain** what it is that you have worked out

▶ **explain** how your answers relate to the problem

▶ **compare** your answers to any statements in the problem

▶ draw **conclusions** based on the comparisons that you have made.

Take a look at this problem:

Let's finish the problem of Glyn and Mair's holiday to Edinburgh.

This is a reminder of the key points and the calculations already done.

Glyn and Mair plan a holiday to Edinburgh.

They plan to go by train from Cardiff to Edinburgh.

They want to take the first train that leaves Cardiff after 10 00 that has one change. They want to come back on the first train that leaves Edinburgh after midday that has one change. They buy the cheapest tickets they can for the times they are travelling.

They book half-board at 'O'Leary's Inn' for one week.

Glyn says, *"The total cost of the train and accommodation is just over £800."*

Is Glyn correct?

Step 1

The total price for the train tickets is $£135 \times 2 = \underline{£270}$ ✓

Check by estimating $£140 \times 2 = \underline{£280}$

Step 2

For one night for Glyn and Mair it would cost $£47 \times 2 = £94$

For seven nights for Glyn and Mair it would cost $£94 \times 7 = \underline{£658}$ ✓

Check by estimating $£50 \times 2 = £100$

$£100 \times 7 = \underline{£700}$

Step 3

The train costs £270 and the accommodation costs £658.

So the total is $£270 + £658 = \underline{£928}$ ✓

Check by estimating $£300 + £700 = \underline{£1,000}$

Now it is time to **interpret** the results.

Explain as fully as you can, what you have worked out and why.

Then compare your answers to the problem you were given. Write down any conclusions that you can make.

For example, you could write

> The problem asked me to work out if Glyn was correct. Glyn says, "The total cost of the train and accommodation is just over £800".
>
> In order to answer this, I needed to work out the total cost of the train, the total cost of the accommodation, and finally the total cost of the holiday.
>
> My calculations show that the total cost of the holiday for Glyn and Mair is £928.
>
> I would say that Glyn's statement is partly correct because £928 is definitely over £800.
>
> However Glyn does say, "just over £800", and I would say that £928 isn't "just over £800". If Glyn had said, "just over £900", then I would say that he was correct, but £928 is £128 over £800. So I am going to say that his statement is incorrect.
>
> Glyn needs to check his calculations and make sure he hasn't used the wrong price for the accommodation. That could be why his total came to "just over £800".

Helpful hints:

- **explain** what it is that you have worked out
- **explain** how your answers relate to the problem you've been asked
- **compare** your answers to any statements in the problem
- draw **conclusions** based on the comparisons that you have made
- don't just write your answers with a 'Yes' or 'No' comment – a full explanation is needed!

The price of eggs

Sally decides to keep chickens and make some money by selling their eggs.

She wants to buy six hens.

Two of the hens will be White Stars.
Two of the hens will be Rhode Island Reds.

The other two hens will be Cochins.

Sally needs to buy a hen house large enough for the six hens.

She is going to sell the eggs for £1.50 for half a dozen.

Sally says, *"If I sell all the eggs I get, it will take me 50 weeks to get the money back that I spent on the hens and their house."*

Is Sally correct?

Help 1

Prices of different breeds of hens

Breed of hen	Price for one hen
White Star	£12
Speckled Star	£12
Black Rock	£15
Rhode Island Red	£18
Cochins	£25
Pekins	£25

Help 2

Facts about hens

A hen lives about 6 years.

A hen's heart beats about 300 times a minute.

A hen will lay about 5 eggs every 7 days for the first 3 years.

A hen must eat about 150 g of food to produce one egg.

A hen's body temperature is about 39 °C.

A hen needs at least 0.4 square metres of indoor space.

1 Find out how much floor space Sally's hens need.

Representing.

2 Find out the floor space of each hen house.

Representing.

3 Decide which hen house Sally should buy.

Interpreting.

4 Work out the total cost of the hens and their house.

Analysing.

5 Work out how many eggs are laid in one week.

Analysing.

6 Work out how many weeks it will take Sally to get the money back that she spent on the hens and their house.

Analysing.

7 Make sure you show how and why you did each calculation at each stage. Make sure you show that you have checked your calculations.

Analysing.

8 Compare your answer with Sally's.

Interpreting.

Help 3

Prices and sizes of different hen houses

Length of house (m)	Width of house (m)	Height of house (m)	Price of house (£)
1.2	1.1	1.2	350
1.4	0.9	1.1	220
2.0	1.1	1.2	295
1.8	1.6	1.0	280
2.1	1.7	1.3	385

Cooking is cool!

Brian has moved house. He is going to cook a meal for himself and three friends to celebrate.

This is his menu.

Menu

Mushroom soup

Cheesy eggs

Crème caramel

Brian says, *"I only need to buy seven ingredients as I already have the rest.*

It should take about 2 hours to prepare and cook the whole meal."

Write a shopping list for Brian.

Are his statements true?

What other things should he add to the list to go with the meal?

Help 1

Mushroom soup (serves 4)	Cheesy eggs (serves 4)	Crème caramel (serves 8)
125 g mushrooms	175 g cheddar cheese	250 g sugar
25 g butter	125 g mushrooms	1.2 *l* full-fat milk
25 g plain flour	40 g plain flour	2.5 m*l* vanilla flavouring
300 m*l* vegetable stock	40 g butter	8 eggs
300 m*l* skimmed milk	30 g Parmesan cheese	
15 m*l* lemon juice	150 m*l* skimmed milk	
30 m*l* double cream	150 m*l* white wine	
	150 m*l* double cream	
	4 eggs	
Cooking time: 15 mins	Cooking time: 15 mins	Cooking time: 1 hour
Preparation time: 15 mins	Preparation time: 20 mins	Preparation time: 20 mins
	Oven temperature: 190°C	Oven temperature: 170°C

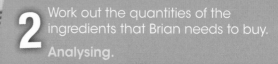
1 Find the total amount that Brian needs of each ingredient.

Representing.

2 Work out the quantities of the ingredients that Brian needs to buy.

Analysing.

3 Write out Brian's shopping list.

Interpreting.

4 Is Brian's first statement correct?

Interpreting.

5 Find the preparation and cooking times of each dish.

Representing.

6 Work out the total time that Brian should take to prepare and cook the meal.

Analysing.

7 Is Brian's second statement correct?

Interpreting.

8 Make sure you show how and why you did each calculation at each stage. Make sure you show that you have checked your calculations.

Analysing.

9 What other things do you think he needs to buy to go with the meal?

Interpreting.

Help 2

Chef's top tips!

Soup can be prepared in advance and reheated before serving.

Chestnut mushrooms tast better than button mushrooms.

One vegetable stock cube will make 200 ml of vegetable stock.

Cheesy eggs must be served straight from the oven.

Fresh Parmesan cheese is much better than dried.

Crème caramel is best made the day before and left in the fridge.

Help 3

In his kitchen, Brian already has:

250 g	butter
150 g	cottage cheese
1 kg	plain flour
½ dozen	eggs
1 kg	self-raising flour
1	vegetable stock cube
2 l	skimmed milk
500 g	sugar
125 g	button mushrooms
1 bottle	red wine
250 ml	single cream
1 l	olive oil
250 ml	double cream
2	tins tomatoes

Riding stables

Lawson runs a riding stable. He has six horses.

The **amount** of food a horse eats each day depends on its weight.

To work out the weight of a horse, Lawson measures the length and the girth of each horse in centimetres. The girth is the distance around a horse's waist. He then uses a table to work out the weight of each horse in kilograms.

The **type** of food given to a horse depends on how much exercise it does.

Horses are fed a mixture of **hay** and a **hard feed** such as oats.

Lawson says *"It costs me over £40 a week to feed the horses."*

Is Lawson correct?

Help 1

The horses

Name	Length (cm)	Girth (cm)	Age (years)	Level of exercise
Lightning	105	160	12	Light
Ernie	115	180	8	Hard
Scooter	100	175	9	Medium
Arizona	115	170	15	Hard
Apache	100	165	18	Medium
Thunder	110	175	12	Light

Help 2

Facts and figures

The height of a horse is measured in hands and inches.

Four inches make one hand.

Lawson doesn't buy hay, he produces his own.

On average a horse drinks 35 litres of water a day.

A 20 kg sack of hard feed costs £6.

Horses like treats such as apples and carrots.

To calculate the total weight of feed that a horse needs each day, use the formula

Amount of feed in kg

= weight of horse in kg ÷ 40

Work it out!

1 Find out the weight of each horse in kilograms.

Representing.

2 Work out the total daily weight of feed for each horse.

Analysing.

3 Find the percentage of the total daily feed that is hard feed for each horse.

Representing.

4 Work out the total weekly weight of hard feed.

Analysing.

5 Work out the weekly cost.

Analysing.

6 Make sure you show and check your calculations.

Are your results sensible?

Analysing.

7 Compare your answer with Lawson's.

Interpreting.

Help 3

This table gives the weight of a horse, in kilograms, by using the girth and length of the horse.

length (cm)	girth (cm)				
	160	165	170	175	180
100	300	320	340	360	380
105	320	340	360	380	400
110	340	360	380	400	420
115	360	380	400	420	440

Help 4

Percentage of total daily feed that is hay and hard feed

Level of exercise	Hay (%)	Hard feed (%)
Light	80	20
Medium	70	30
Hard	60	40

In a jam!

A farmer makes jam from the fruit he grows.
He sells it over the internet to small shops.

He completes a bill for each of his customers.

The bill shows the total cost of the jam and the cost of delivery.

The farmer uses two delivery companies.

Both companies work out the delivery charge by measuring the weight of the parcel he sends.

The farmer always chooses the cheapest company.

Here are the orders the farmer gets one day.

| Name of customer | Number of jars of jam | | | Type of delivery |
	Strawberry	Raspberry	Blackberry	
Mr Wilson	卌 I	IIII	卌 III	Next day
Mrs Slater	卌 卌 I	卌 III	卌 卌	Standard
Mrs Hoyle	IIII	II	卌 II	Standard

The farmer says, "*Mrs Slater's bill is more than Mr Wilson's and Mrs Hoyle's bills added together.*"

Is the farmer correct?

Help 1

Price list

Flavour	Weight of jar (g)	Price per jar (£)
Strawberry	400	2.85
Blackcurrant	400	2.95
Redcurrant	400	2.95
Raspberry	600	3.05
Plum	600	3.10
Blackberry	600	3.15

Help 2

Delivery charges

Company: Parcels 'R' Us		
Weight (kg) up to:	**Standard delivery (£)**	**Next day delivery (£)**
5	8.70	12.50
10	14.40	24.65
12	16.80	25.70
14	18.55	28.95
16	22.95	30.78

Company: Stand and Deliver		
Weight (kg) up to:	**Standard delivery (£)**	**Next day delivery (£)**
2	4.20	8.25
4	6.85	13.60
6	9.30	22.00
8	11.40	24.30
10	12.24	26.50
15	14.26	32.20
20	21.95	40.54

1 Find the number of jars of jam ordered by each customer.
Representing.

2 Work out the total cost of the jam for each customer.
Analysing.

3 Work out the weight of each parcel.
Analysing.

4 Find the delivery charge for each parcel.
Representing.

5 Find the total cost of each bill.
Analysing.

6 Make sure you show and check your calculations.
Are your results sensible?
Analysing.

7 Is the farmer correct?
Interpreting.

Help 3

Useful information

A box that holds 18 jars of jam weighs 350 g.

This box measures 21 cm long by 21 cm wide by 18 cm high.

A box that holds 32 jars of jam weighs 450 g.

This box measures 28 cm long by 28 cm wide by 18 cm high.

All boxes containing glass must have a 'Fragile' label.

All the boxes are made from 80% recycled paper.

Spring lambs

Alistair is a sheep farmer in Scotland.

He keeps a record of how many lambs he sends to market and the total weight of these lambs. He also records the total weight of meat they produce and the price he is paid for the meat.

Alistair makes these three statements.

*"In May I was always paid **more** per kilogram of meat than the national average."*

"In the week of 26 May, the mean weight of the lambs was higher than any other week."

"My lambs were in very good condition three out of the four weeks that I sent them to the market."

Are Alistair's statements correct?

Help 1

Alistair's records

Date	Number of lambs sent to market	Total weight (kg)	Total weight of meat (kg)	Total price paid for the meat (£)
5 May	9	315	130	257.40
12 May	10	340	146	268.64
19 May	22	792	340	652.80
26 May	17	646	245	465.50

Help 2

Lamb facts

A sheep will eat 4% of its bodyweight in feed each day.

The total number of lambs in the UK in 2007 was 16 855 000.

A lamb goes to market when it is between $2\frac{1}{2}$ and 3 months old.

To work out the condition of the lambs, multiply the weight by 0.4.

If this value is less than the weight of meat, the lamb is in very good condition.

Hint 1

Work out the price per kilogram of meat that Alistair was paid each week.

Hint 2

To find the weekly mean weight, divide the total weight by the number of lambs sent to market.

Hint 3

Remember to show your calculations and explain what you are doing and why you're doing it.

Help 3

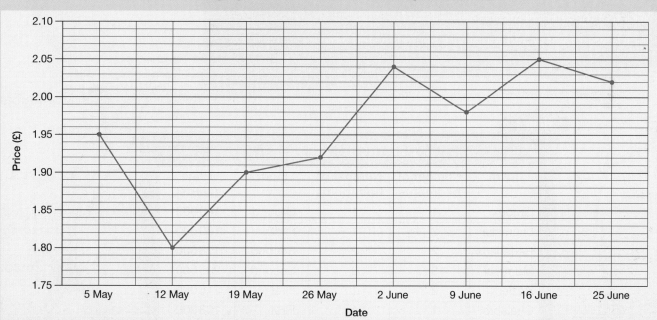

UK average price of lamb meat May–June 2008

Price (£) axis: 1.75, 1.80, 1.85, 1.90, 1.95, 2.00, 2.05, 2.10	Date axis: 5 May, 12 May, 19 May, 26 May, 2 June, 9 June, 16 June, 25 June

Moving back to France

Marie moved from France to the UK because of her job five years ago. In 2008 she decides to move back to France and buy an apartment.

This is her wish list.

> The apartment must be
> - no more than 120 Km from Toulouse airport
> - no more than 90 Km from the sea
> - less than £145 000.
>
> The apartment must have at least 2 bedrooms.
> It must not be a ground floor apartment.

Which of the apartments suit her wish list?

Which apartment would you advise her to buy and why?

Cahors ●

● Montauban

Help 1

Apartments for sale

Town	Number of bedrooms	Number of bathrooms	Floor	Price (euros)
Limoux	1	1	Ground	140 000
Lagrasse	2	1	First	180 000
Bédarieux	2	2	Second	178 000
Montréal	3	2	Second	205 000
Béziers	2	1	First	215 000
Chalabre	1	1	First	168 000
Mazamet	3	1	Ground	190 000
Pézenas	2	2	Second	184 000
Alzonne	2	2	First	172 000
Lacaune	2	1	Second	164 000

Toulouse

N113

A66

D 29

A 43 (GRENOBLE) péage

✈ SAINT EXUPÉRY

🚚 GENAS

MEYZIEU

Parc des Activités - les Marches du Rhône

Help 2

Useful information

In Sept 2008 you could convert a price from euros (€) to pounds (£) by dividing by 1.25. You could convert a price from pounds (£) to euros (€) by multiplying by 1.25.

Toulouse airport is to the west of Toulouse.
The A61-E80 is the motorway from Toulouse to Narbonne.
The N113 is the main road from Toulouse to Narbonne.
The map has a scale of 1 cm = 10 km.

Resource sheet 1 provides a simplified version of the map to work from.

Hint 1

Work out the maximum price that Marie can spend in euros.

Hint 2

Find the apartments that have at least two bedrooms, aren't on the ground floor, and are less than her maximum price.

Rodez

Albi

Lacaune

Bédarieux

Montpellier

Castres ✈

N113

Pézenas

Mazamet

Béziers

✈

N113

Alzonne

Carcassonne ✈

N113

E80

Montréal

Narbonne

Lagrasse

Camping with wolves

As part of his Duke of Edinburgh award, Carlos has decided to go to the Carpathian Mountains in Romania to help with a wolf conservation project.

He will be camping while helping with the project.

He books the afternoon flight from London, Heathrow, on Saturday 22 March.

His return flight is on Saturday 29 March.

Before he leaves Carlos plans to buy

▶ the lightest tent he can find
▶ the cheapest sleeping bag that will be warm enough at night
▶ £115 of euros
▶ other camping equipment costing a total of £76.

Carlos says, "If I round all the prices to the nearest £10, I estimate the total cost of the camping trip is going to be £650."

Is Carlos correct?

Hint 1

Make sure that you look very carefully at the tables and ignore the information that you don't need.

Hint 2

Be careful to round off the amounts that you need to the nearest £10.

Help 1

Flight prices from London Heathrow (LHR) and London Gatwick (LGW) to Romania

Depart	Date	Time	Return flight price (£)
LHR	Sat 15 Mar	06 50	195
LGW	Sat 15 Mar	13 40	195
LHR	Sat 15 Mar	18 30	215
LHR	Sat 22 Mar	06 50	234
LGW	Sat 22 Mar	13 40	220
LHR	Sat 22 Mar	18 30	242

Help 2

Tent information

Name of tent	Weight (kg)	Pack dimensions (cm)	Price (£)
Spirit	2.4	49 × 15	199.99
Comfort	2.5	60 × 20	29.99
Backpack	2.8	51 × 14	39.99
Quickpitch	2.05	49 × 10	59.99
Alpha	3.15	8 × 88	79.99

Help 3

Sleeping bag information

Name of sleeping bag	Lowest temperature (°C)	Pack dimensions (cm)	Price (£)
Adventurer	−7	30 × 18	54.99
Snuggler	−1	44 × 22	16.99
Ice-warm	−7	35 × 20	24.99
Blue skies	0	45 × 20	14.99

Help 4

Lowest night-time temperature in the Carpathian Mountains

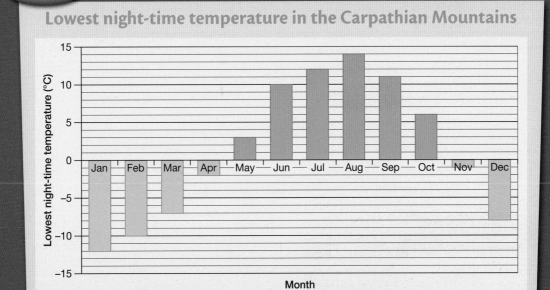

Litter bugs!

Ros is a marine biologist and is concerned by the state of beaches around the UK. Every September she takes part in a beach litter survey.

She compares the types of litter found on the beaches in England, Scotland, Wales and Northern Ireland in 2008.

Ros says, *"In each country most of the litter comes from beach visitors.*
England had the most amount of litter per kilometre of beach.
The mean number of items of litter per volunteer was highest in Wales."

Are Ros's statements correct? Explain your answers.

Help 1

Beach litter survey details for 2008

Country	Number of beaches surveyed	Total number of volunteers	Total number of items of litter	Total length of beach surveyed (km)
Northern Ireland	5	60	5040	5
Scotland	48	560	43 120	16
Wales	37	495	41 085	15
England	224	2490	229 080	115

Help 2

Useful information

The beach litter survey took place on 16 and 17 September.

346 120 items of litter were collected from the beaches in the UK.

2780 bags were used.

The amount of litter per kilometre is found using the formula

$$\text{Amount of litter per km} = \frac{\text{total number of items of litter}}{\text{total length of beach surveyed}}.$$

The volunteers took over 8300 hours to collect all the litter.

Over 50% of all the litter collected was plastic.

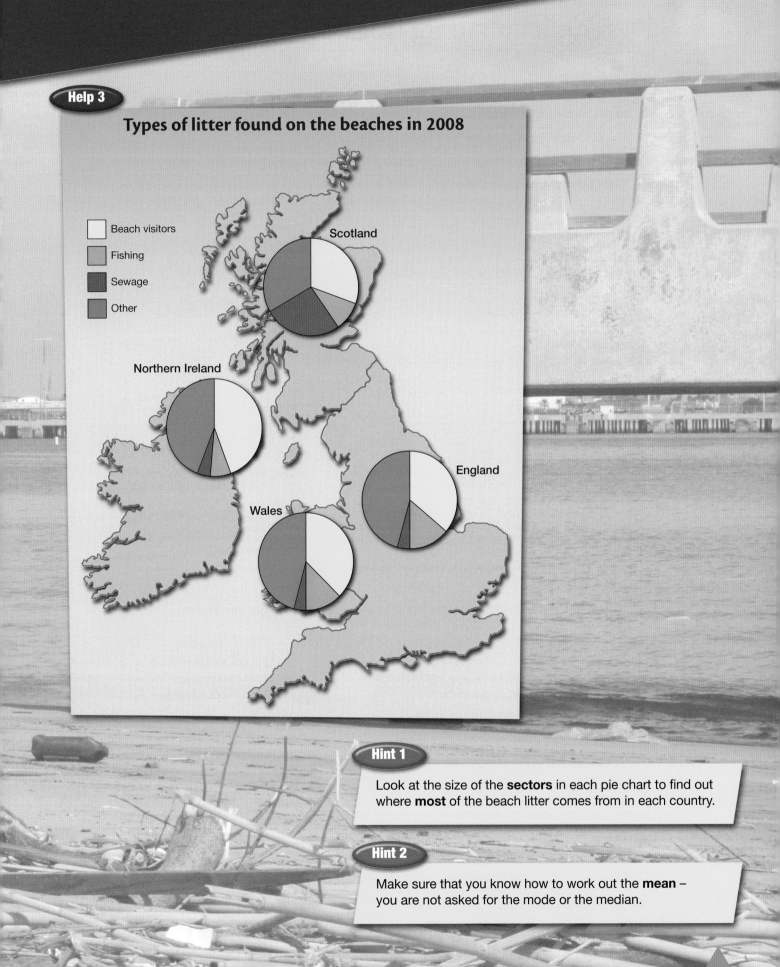

Types of litter found on the beaches in 2008

Beach visitors

Fishing

Sewage

Other

Scotland

Northern Ireland

England

Wales

Look at the size of the **sectors** in each pie chart to find out where **most** of the beach litter comes from in each country.

Make sure that you know how to work out the **mean** – you are not asked for the mode or the median.

Swimming pool

At a swimming pool, adults can buy a swimming card.

This card allows them to swim for free for one year.

Adults without a swimming card, and all children, have to pay each time they use the pool.

Every week the manager of the swimming pool works out how much money has been taken.

Pictogram to show the number of people using the swimming pool in the first week of September

Key:  represents 40 people

Monday	
Tuesday	
Wednesday	
Thursday	
Friday	
Saturday	
Sunday	

Manager's notes

In the first week of September:

25% of swimmers were adults.

Two new swimming cards were sold.

½ of all the adults had a swimming card.

50% of swimmers stayed in for over an hour.

30% of swimmers were female.

¼ of all the swimmers came on their own.

(a) How many adults and how many children used the swimming pool in the first week of September?

You must show your calculations and state how you used them to get your answer.

Swimming pool
opening times

| Mon–Fri | 7 am–9 pm |
| Sat–Sun | 8 am–6 pm |

Early morning swim (adults only)
| Mon–Fri | 7 am–9 am |

Swimming club (children only)
| Sat–Sun | 11 am–1 pm |

Swimming pool
price list

Adult yearly swimming card		£180
Price per swim:		
January to June	Adults	£2.20
	Children	£1.50
July to December	Adults	£2.40
	Children	£1.70

The manager says, *"In the first week of September, we took over £1400."*

(b) Is the manager correct?

You must show your calculations and state how you used them to get your answer.

Look through the following answers written by a student.

See if you can allocate the examiner's comments to the correct parts of the student's answers.

(a)

A First of all I need to work out the total number of people who used the pool in the first week of September. I will find out this information from the pictogram. Then I will use the manager's notes to work out the number of adults and the number of children who used the pool.

B From the pictogram I can see that ▦ = 40 people,

so ▢ = 10 people, ▤ = 20 people and ⬓ = 30 people.

The total number of people who used the pool in the week was 680.

C From the manager's notes I can see that 25% of all the swimmers were adults, so

$$0.25 \times 680 = 170. \quad \text{There were 170 adults.}$$
$$680 - 170 = 510. \quad \text{There were 510 children.}$$

To check: 25% is the same as $\frac{1}{4}$, 680 is approximately 700, so $\frac{1}{4}$ of 700 is: $700 \div 2 = 350 \div 2 = 175 \approx 170$.

1 Examiner says...
Student has correctly interpreted their answer.

2 Examiner says...
Student hasn't included the two new swimming cards sold.

3 Examiner says...
Incomplete check.

4 Examiner says...
Student has interpreted the pictogram correctly, but hasn't shown all workings.

(b)

D First of all I need to work out how many adults didn't have a swimming card. Then I need to work out the money paid by adults and the money paid by children.

E
$$\frac{1}{2} \text{ of } 170 = 85$$
$$85 \times £2.40 = £204$$
$$510 \times £1.70 = £867$$
$$£204 + £867 = £1071$$

To check:
$$90 \times £2 = £180$$
$$500 \times £2 = £1000$$
$$£180 + £1000 = £1180 \approx £1071$$

F The manager is wrong. The swimming pool took a total of £1071, which is not over £1400.

5 Examiner says...
Very good plan.

6 Examiner says...
Incomplete plan.

American dream

The Anderson family is planning to go on holiday to America.

They plan to rent an apartment for two weeks in December 2007.

They look at six possible apartments in different cities.

They want the minimum temperature in the city to be higher than −5°C.

In a holiday brochure they see these thermometers showing the maximum and minimum temperatures for December.

(a) Which cities have a minimum temperature that is higher than −5°C?

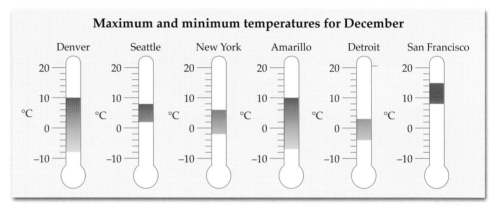

Maximum and minimum temperatures for December

The same holiday brochure shows these rainfall charts.

The family want to go somewhere with less than 10 cm of rain in December.

They want the apartment to have two bedrooms.

They can pay up to £350 per week for the apartment.

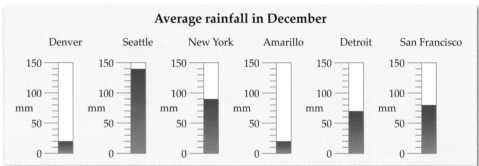

Average rainfall in December

Apartment details

City	1 bed	2 bed	3 bed	1 bath	2 bath	pool	$/week
Denver			✔		✔		800
Seattle	✔			✔		✔	600
New York		✔			✔	✔	750
Amarillo		✔			✔	✔	650
Detroit		✔			✔	✔	650
San Francisco		✔		✔			650

Useful information

- The time in Seattle is 8 hours behind the time in the UK.
- The time in New York is 5 hours behind the time in the UK.
- Although it varies, on this occasion, to change an amount in pounds to an amount in dollars, multiply by 2.
- Although it varies, on this occasion, to change an amount in dollars to an amount in pounds, divide by 2.
- Denver is called the 'mile high city' as it is 1 mile above sea level.
- The Golden Gate Bridge is found in San Francisco.

(b) Which apartment should they choose?

You must show any calculations that you do, and give reasons for your answers.

You're the examiner!

Look through the following answers written by a student.

See if you can allocate the examiner's comments to the correct parts of the student's answers.

(a)

A First of all I need to read the thermometers and work out the maximum and minimum temperatures in each of the cities.

Maximums:

Denver	10°C	Seattle	8°C	New York	6°C
Amarillo	10°C	Detroit	3°C	San Francisco	15°C

Minimums:

Denver	−8°C	Seattle	2°C	New York	−2°C
Amarillo	−7°C	Detroit	−4°C	San Francisco	8°C

B I can see that Seattle, New York, Detroit and San Francisco all have minimum temperatures higher than −5°C.

(b)

C First of all I need to find the rainfall in Seattle, New York, Detroit and San Francisco; I don't need to do Denver and Amarillo because those cities are too cold. Then I need to find from the table which apartments have two bedrooms. I finally need to convert £350 into dollars so I can see which apartments the Andersons can afford.

Rainfall:

Seattle	140 mm	New York	90 mm
Detroit	70 mm	San Francisco	80 mm

D The family wants their city to have less than 10 cm of rain.

10 cm = 100 mm; Seattle has more than 100 mm, so New York, Detroit and San Francisco are all possibilities.

If I look at the apartment details I see that New York, Detroit and San Francisco all have two bedrooms, so any of these are fine.

E £350 × 2 = $700, so the Andersons can spend $1400 dollars. This means that they can afford any of the three apartments.

F The Anderson family could choose the New York, Detroit or San Francisco apartment. The New York and Detroit apartments are better as they have two bathrooms and a pool, whereas the San Francisco apartment only has one bathroom and no pool. The temperature in San Francisco, however, is likely to be warmer than Detroit and New York, but in New York there could be more rain, and the apartment is the most expensive. I would choose San Francisco as I'd like it to be warmer and I'd like to see the Golden Gate Bridge.

---

1 **Examiner says…**
Correct conversion of cm into mm.

2 **Examiner says…**
Very good plan.

3 **Examiner says…**
Incorrect interpretation of $/week column in table.

4 **Examiner says…**
This information is not needed.

5 **Examiner says…**
Student has interpreted their answers correctly.

6 **Examiner says…**
Student has correctly understood negative numbers in context.

Business trip

Richard has to organise a business trip to the USA during the first six months of next year.

He wants to choose a month with the lowest rainfall and an average daily temperature of more than 25°C.

He sees this table on the internet, and uses it to decide which month to travel.

Month	J	F	M	A	M	J	J	A	S	O	N	D
Average daily temperature (°C)	23	23	26	27	30	31	32	31	31	28	27	25
Average monthly rainfall (mm)	5.6	3.8	4.7	5.2	8.8	11.6	8.3	13.7	13.8	11.0	6.7	5.4

(a) Which month should Richard choose? [2 marks]

(b) What is the range of rainfall in the table? [2 marks]

Richard lives near Tewkesbury. He can fly to the USA from Cardiff, Heathrow and Bristol airports.

Richard must consider the cost of driving to and from the airport, the parking fees and the flight fuel surcharge.

When Richard uses his car he allows 30p per mile to cover petrol costs.

Airport	Distance from home (miles)	Parking costs (£)	Flight fuel surcharge (£)
Cardiff	90	40	30
Heathrow	110	90	20
Bristol	40	75	40

(c) Use the information above to decide which airport would be cheapest overall to fly from.

You must show your calculations. [12 marks]

Tasty tapas!

Miguel runs a tapas bar where he sells home made Spanish food.

Today he is making 'chorizo al vino' and 'chorizo con patatas'.

Miguel has 1.5 litres of red wine. To make 'chorizo al vino' he needs to add water to the wine before cooking. The amount of water has to be half the volume of the wine.

(a) How much water does he need? [2 marks]

The amounts of cider, potatoes and chorizo Miguel uses to make 8 servings of 'chorizo con patatas' are shown in the recipe below.

CHORIZO CON PATATAS
serves 8

325 ml	cider
425 g	potatoes
240 g	chorizo sausage

Miguel wants to make 56 servings.

(b) How much cider, potato and chorizo sausage does he need to make 56 servings?

You must show your calculations. [4 marks]

Miguel thinks that fresh orange juice is more popular than alcohol-free beer in the evening. He also thinks that he has more customers between 7 pm and 8 pm than at any other time in the evening. He keeps a tally of the fresh orange juice and alcohol-free beer he sells to check if this is correct.

	Early evening time slots			
	1701–1800	**1801–1900**	**1901–2000**	**2001–2100**
Fresh orange juice	||| ||	||| ||| ||| |||		||| ||| ||| ||| ||| |||		||| ||| ||| ||| ||
Alcohol-free beer	||| ||| ||| |||	||| ||||	||| ||| |||	||| ||| |||	

(c) Find out if Miguel is correct and use graph paper to show Miguel's information. [10 marks]

www.HygenicAnti-slipFlooring.co.uk

Tough and hygienic: coin anti-slip flooring on a roll (USA made)

Width: 4.6 m   Length: any (max length 22.8 m)   Cost: £22 per m²

Tough and hygienic: coin anti-slip flooring on a roll (USA made)

Width: 3.7 m   Length: any (max length 22.8 m)   Cost: £22 per m²

Please note: we advise all of our customers to add 10 cm to the length of roll needed e.g. if you need a 5.5 m length, please order a 5.6 m length.

Emily needs to buy new flooring for the operating theatre of the doctor's surgery she works in.

This is a plan of the operating theatre.

- The flooring must be in one piece.
- The flooring must fit the room, wall-to-wall.

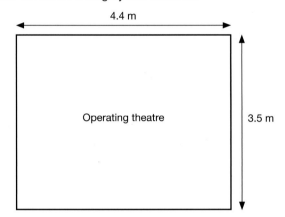

4.4 m

Operating theatre

3.5 m

Emily works out that there are two ways that she can buy just enough flooring.

(a) Draw two sketches. Use one sketch to show how the flooring would fit if she bought it from the 4.6 m roll and the other sketch to show how the flooring would fit if Emily bought it from the 3.7 m roll. Shade the flooring that must be cut off and wasted. Remember to include the measurements of the flooring.

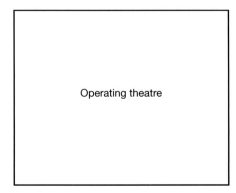

Operating theatre

Operating theatre

[6 marks]

(b) Which of these two ways of buying the flooring would be cheaper for Emily?

You must show your calculations and state how you used them to get your answer.   **[10 marks]**

Light work!

Ian takes over a new office for his graphic design business.

This is the floor plan of the new office.

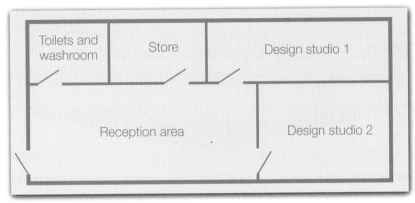

- Each room has a centre light except the toilet and washroom.
- There are 3 wall lights in the toilet and washroom and 2 wall lights in design studio 1.
- There are 3 computer lamps in design studio 2.
- There is 1 desk lamp in design studio 1.
- All the bulbs in the office are conventional light bulbs.

Ian plans to replace the conventional light bulbs with energy saving bulbs.

(a) Use the table to make a list of conventional bulbs that Ian needs for his new office.

Conventional bulbs (watts)	Office/workplace use
40	Low level security lighting
60	Mood lighting in relaxation area
100	Desk lamp, computer lamp
150	Down light, wall light, centre light
180	Spot light

[2 marks]

This table shows the energy saving bulbs that can be used to replace conventional bulbs.

Conventional bulbs (watts)	Energy saving bulbs (watts)
40	10
60	15–18
100	50 (halogen), OR 18 (low energy spiral)
150	26–30
180	35–40

(b) List the energy saving bulbs that Ian needs to replace his conventional bulbs.   **[2 marks]**

(c) Ian thinks that, when he has all of the lights on, he can save over 1400 watts of power by replacing the conventional bulbs with energy saving bulbs. Is he right?   **[12 marks]**

Introduction

Take a look at this problem:

Grandpa John lives in Stanford-le-Hope in Essex and his grandson Joe is putting down a new lawn for him at the beginning of July. John is on metered water, so he plans to store the rainwater falling on his conservatory roof and then use it to water the new lawn.

In one of Grandpa John's old gardening books Joe finds several useful pieces of information.

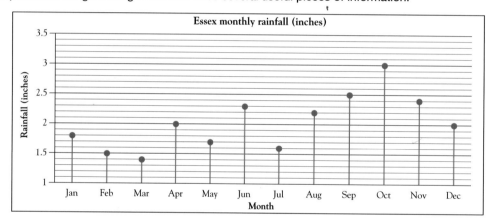

Essex monthly rainfall (inches)

- To find the volume of rainwater collected, this formula is used

  Volume of rainwater in gallons = $\dfrac{\text{footprint of roof (ft}^2) \times \text{rainfall (inches)}}{2.12}$

- The footprint of a roof is the ground area of the building.

  The footprint of John's conservatory is a rectangle 10 feet by 17 feet.

John collects rainwater in a large tank from the beginning of February until the beginning of June and saves it for watering his new lawn. All the water collected from the conservatory goes into the water tank. There is no evaporation.

According to Joe, John's new lawn will be a rectangle measuring 12 m by 8 m and each 8 m by 1 m strip will need 20 litres of water every week in addition to normal rainfall.

John and Joe know that a gallon is an imperial measure and a litre is a metric measure. In another gardening book John finds that 1 gallon = 4.55 litres and some other information.

Volume/capacity	
1 inch^3 = 16.4 cm^3	1 cm^3 = 0.061 inches^3
1 pint = 0.57 litres	1 litre = 1.76 pints
1 pint = 0.125 gallons	1 litre = 0.001 m^3
1 gallon = 8 pints	1 m^3 = 1000 litres

Ignore any water John collects in June and July. Work out if John can save enough rainwater between 1 February and 1 June to water his new lawn until the end of July.

You must show your calculations and state how you have used them to get your answer.

[18 marks]

Yes, he has 10 weeks worth of watering in the tank.

Plan:

✓ Use rainfall chart to calculate total rainfall, in inches, saved in water tank from 1 February to 1 June.

✓ Find volume of rainfall, in gallons, saved in water tank from 1 February to 1 June.

✓ Change volume of water saved in water tank from gallons to litres.

✓ Calculate the water that the new lawn needs from 1 June to end of July.

✓ Say whether there is enough water.

● Use the rainfall chart to calculate total rainfall from 1 February to 1 June.
I need to know this to be able to work out the total volume of water in the tank.
Rainfall = 1.5 + 1.4 + 2.0 + 1.7 = 6.6 inches

● Use the formula to calculate the total volume of water in the tank.

$$\text{Volume} = \frac{10 \times 17 \times 6.6}{2.12} = 529.245\ldots \text{ gallons.}$$

● Change number of gallons to litres. I need to know how many litres of water are saved to compare with the amount of water needed for the new lawn.

$529.245\ldots$ gallons × 4.55 = 2408.06... litres

● Calculate the amount of water the new lawn needs from 1 June to end of July.

　● An 8 m by 1 m strip needs 20 litres per week
　There are 12 strips 8 m by 1 m
　Water needed per week = 12 × 20 = 240 litres

　● Number of weeks from 1 June to end of July
　June = 30 days, July = 31 days, Total = 30 + 31 = 61 days
　Number of weeks = 61 ÷ 7 = 8.7... = about 9

　● Total water needed = 9 × 240 = 2160 litres

● Conclusion:
John should have 2400 litres of water saved (if the figures are accurate and the year has an average rainfall).

John needs 2160 litres to water the new lawn (if he is careful to only use the water that he should) from 1 June to the end of July.

He should have enough water for the new lawn – he should have about 240 litres left, enough for another week of watering.

Representing

What is representing?

Representing is 'making sense of situations and representing them'.
You need to be able to look at a problem and work out what you should do to solve it.

You need to decide

▶ what pieces of the information you **need**

▶ what pieces of the information you **don't need**

▶ what mathematical **techniques** you need to use
e.g. addition, subtraction, finding the mean or the range

▶ what **order** to work things out in to solve the problem.

Take a look at this problem:

John decides it is time to lose weight and get fit.

He is 180 cm tall. At the moment he weighs 100 kg.

He changes his diet to eat more healthily and he joins a gym.

John says, *"If I try to lose $1\frac{1}{2}$ kilograms in weight each week, it will take me about four months to get my weight down into the Okay weight category.*

Also, if I go to the gym every morning and keep to my exercise plan, I will easily burn off the calories I ate at breakfast."

Is John correct?

John's breakfast

30 g	cornflakes	OR	75 g	porridge
300 ml	skimmed milk		300 ml	semi-skimmed milk
100 g	banana		150 g	toast
250 ml	orange juice		20 g	butter
	black coffee			black coffee

Calorie chart

Calories per 100 g of food	
apple	45
banana	74
bread	140
butter	750
branflakes	330
coffee (black)	0
cornflakes	360
honey	288
jam	262
porridge	372
yoghurt	68
apple juice (100 ml)	42
orange juice (100 ml)	34
milk:	
skimmed (100 ml)	36
semi-skimmed (100 ml)	50
full cream (100 ml)	65

Calories used per minute

Gentle exercise	4
Walking	6
Cycling	7
Running	8
Rowing	8
Stepping	9
Cross training	9
Skipping	10

John's exercise plan

Activity/ machine	Time (mins)
Warm up	10
Walking	20
Cycling	20
Rowing	10
Cool down	10

Height/weight chart

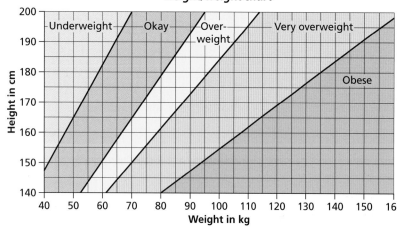

Helpful hints:

Before you start doing any calculations

● write down a plan

● highlight the information that you **need**

● cross out the information that you **don't need**

● write down what **techniques** you need to use

● write down the **order** you are going to do things in.

To answer this problem, first highlight the important pieces of information from the introduction.

John decides it is time to lose weight and get fit.

He is 180 cm tall. At the moment he weighs 100 kg.

He changes his diet to eat more healthily and he joins a gym.

John says, "If I try to lose $1\frac{1}{2}$ kilograms in weight each week, it will take me about four months to get my weight down into the Okay weight category.

Also, if I go to the gym every morning and keep to my exercise plan, I will easily burn off the calories I ate at breakfast."

Is John correct?

Next find where John is on the height/weight chart.

He is in the Very overweight section.

To get his weight down to the Okay section you can see that he needs to lose about 20 kg.

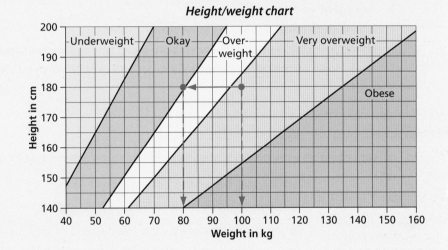

Height/weight chart

Now look at the other information you are given and cross out information you **don't need**.

Cross out the foods that John doesn't eat for breakfast and cross out the activities that aren't part of his exercise plan ('warm up' and 'cool down' are gentle exercise).

Calorie chart

Calories per 100 g of food	
~~apple~~	45
banana	74
bread	140
butter	750
~~branflakes~~	330
coffee (black)	0
cornflakes	360
~~honey~~	288
~~jam~~	262
porridge	372
~~yoghurt~~	68
~~apple juice~~ (100 ml)	42
orange juice(100 ml)	34
milk:	
skimmed (100 ml)	36
semi-skimmed (100 ml)	50
~~full cream~~ (100 ml)	65

Calories used per minute

Activity	Calories
Gentle exercise	4
Walking	6
Cycling	7
~~Running~~	8
Rowing	8
~~Stepping~~	9
~~Cross training~~	9
~~Skipping~~	10

Now that you have all the information you **need**, what **techniques** will you use and in what **order** are you going to work things out?

Here is one way you could work out the answers.

▶ Use the height/weight chart to work out if John's first statement is correct.

▶ Work out how many calories are in each of John's breakfasts (use , ÷ and +).

▶ Work out how many calories John uses if he keeps to his exercise plan (use and +).

Process Skills
Analysing

Analysing is 'processing and using the mathematics'.

You need to be able to use the techniques you said you would use in your **representing** plan, and correctly work out the answers.

You need to

▶ **be organised** and follow your plan

▶ use mathematical techniques to **work out** answers

▶ **check** your calculations at every stage to make sure the answers make sense

▶ **write down** all the calculations that you do, and explain why you are doing them.

Take a look at this problem:

Let's continue with John's weight loss problem. This is a reminder of the key points.

John decides it is time to lose weight and get fit.

He is 180 cm tall. At the moment he weighs 100 kg.

He changes his diet to eat more healthily and he joins a gym.

John says, *"If I try to lose $1\frac{1}{2}$ kilograms in weight each week, it will take me about four months to get my weight down into the Okay weight category.*

Also, if I go to the gym every morning and keep to my exercise plan, I will easily burn off the calories I ate at breakfast."

Is John correct?

In the **representing** section, this was the plan you could follow.

▶ Use the height/weight chart to work out if John's first statement is correct.

▶ Work out how many calories are in each of John's breakfasts (use ×, ÷ and +).

▶ Work out how many calories John uses if he keeps to his exercise plan (use × and +).

Helpful hints:

Follow your plan and
- **organise** your work so that you can follow it, and more importantly so that other people can follow it too
- **write down** what you are finding at every stage
- **work out** your answers accurately
- **check** your calculations at every stage
- **write down** all the calculations that you do
- **write down** all the checks that you do
- don't worry if you have to change your plan part way through the problem – just make sure you **write down** what you have changed and why you have changed it.

Step 1

John needs to lose about 20 kg to get into the Okay weight category.

If he loses $1\frac{1}{2}$ kg each week it will take him	$20 \div 1\frac{1}{2} = 13\frac{1}{3}$ weeks
The total number of days in 4 months is	$31 \times 4 = 124$ days
There are 7 days in a week, so the total number of weeks is	$124 \div 7 = 17.7 \approx \underline{\textbf{18}}$ weeks ✓
Check by estimating	$30 \times 4 = 120$ days
	$120 \div 6 = \underline{\textbf{20}}$ weeks

Step 2

When working out the calories notice that the chart shows numbers for 100 g or 100 ml of food.

30 g	cornflakes	$36 \times 3 = 108$
300 ml	skimmed milk	$36 \times 3 = 108$
100 g	banana	$= 74$
250 ml	orange juice	$34 \times 2.5 = 85$
	black coffee	$= 0$
	Total:	$\underline{\textbf{375}}$ ✓

Check by estimating $40 \times 3 = 120$, $30 \times 3 = 90$
$120 + 120 + 70 + 90 = \underline{\textbf{400}}$

75 g	porridge	$372 \times 0.75 = 279$
300 ml	semi-skimmed milk	$50 \times 3 = 150$
150 g	toast	$140 \times 1.5 = 210$
20 g	butter	$750 \times 0.2 = 150$
	black coffee	$= 0$
	Total:	$\underline{\textbf{789}}$ ✓

Check by estimating $400 \times 0.75 = 300$, $50 \times 3 = 150$, $100 \times 2 = 200$, $800 \times 0.2 = 160$
$300 + 150 + 200 + 160 = \underline{\textbf{810}}$

Calorie chart

Calories per 100 g of food	
apple	45
banana	74
bread	140
butter	750
branflakes	330
coffee (black)	0
cornflakes	360
honey	288
jam	262
porridge	372
yoghurt	68
apple juice (100 ml)	42
orange juice (100 ml)	34
milk:	
skimmed (100 ml)	36
semi-skimmed (100 ml)	50
full cream (100 ml)	65

Step 3

Work out how many calories John uses if he keeps to his exercise plan.
Notice that the calories used in the activities are per minute.

Activity/ machine	Time (mins)	
Warm up	10	$10 \times 4 = 40$
Walking	20	$20 \times 6 = 120$
Cycling	20	$20 \times 7 = 140$
Rowing	10	$10 \times 8 = 80$
Cool down	10	$10 \times 4 = 40$
	Total:	$\underline{\textbf{440}}$ ✓

Calories used per minute

Activity	Calories
Gentle exercise	4
Walking	6
Cycling	7
Running	8
Rowing	8
Stepping	9
Cross-training	9
Skipping	10

Now check by estimating $50 + 100 + 100 + 100 + 50 = \underline{\textbf{400}}$

It is important to note at this stage that the plan you followed isn't the only plan possible.
You could have followed this plan for instance.

▶ Use the height/weight chart to work out if John's first statement is correct.

▶ Work out how many calories John uses if he keeps to his exercise plan (use × and +).

▶ Work out how many calories are in each of John's breakfasts (use ×, ÷ and +).

In this case it doesn't matter what you work out first, the calories he eats or the calories he uses. You need both to work out the final step but you can do them in whatever order you like.

Process Skills
Interpreting

What is interpreting?

Interpreting is 'interpreting and communicating the results of the analysis'.

You need to be able to use the answers to the calculations you have done to explain clearly what the answers mean, and how they relate to the problem you've been asked to solve.

You need to

▶ **explain** what it is that you have worked out

▶ **explain** how your answers relate to the problem you've been asked to solve

▶ **compare** your answers to any statements in the problem

▶ draw **conclusions** based on the comparisons that you have made.

Take a look at this problem:

Let's finish John's weight loss problem.

This is a reminder of the key points and the calculations already done:

John decides it is time to lose weight and get fit.

He is 180 cm tall. At the moment he weighs 100 kg.

He changes his diet to eat more healthily and he joins a gym.

John says, "If I try to lose $1\frac{1}{2}$ kilograms in weight each week, it will take me about four months to get my weight down into the Okay weight category.

Also, if I go to the gym every morning and keep to my exercise plan, I will easily burn off the calories I ate at breakfast."

Is John correct?

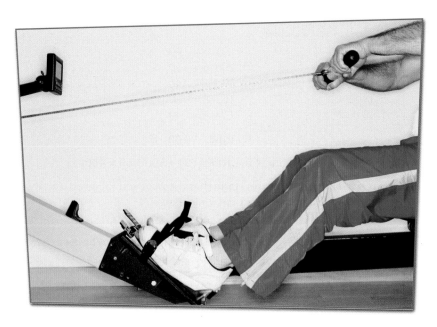

Step 1

If he loses $1\frac{1}{2}$ kg each week it will take him

The total number of days in 4 months is

There are 7 days in a week, so the total number of weeks is

$20 \div 1\frac{1}{2} = 13\frac{1}{3}$ weeks

$31 \times 4 = 124$ days

$124 \div 7 = 17.7 \approx \underline{\textbf{18}}$ weeks ✓

Step 2

Work out how many calories are in each of John's breakfasts.

30 g	cornflakes	$36 \times 3 = 108$	75 g	porridge	$372 \times 0.75 = 279$
300 ml	skimmed milk	$36 \times 3 = 108$	300 ml	semi-skimmed milk	$50 \times 3 = 150$
100 g	banana	$= 74$	150 g	toast	$140 \times 1.5 = 210$
250 ml	orange juice	$34 \times 2.5 = 85$	20 g	butter	$750 \times 0.2 = 150$
	black coffee	$= 0$		black coffee	$= 0$
		Total: **375** ✓			Total: **789** ✓

Step 3

Activity/ machine	Time (mins)	
Warm up	10	$10 \times 4 = 40$
Walking	20	$20 \times 6 = 120$
Cycling	20	$20 \times 7 = 140$
Rowing	10	$10 \times 8 = 80$
Cool down	10	$10 \times 4 = 40$

Total: **440** ✓

Now it is time to interpret the results.
Explain, as fully as you can, what you have worked out and why.
Then compare your answers to the initial problem and write down any conclusions you make.

For example, you could write:

The problem asked me to work out if John was correct.

The first thing he says is, "If I try to lose $1\frac{1}{2}$ kilograms in weight each week, it will take me about four months to get my weight down into the Okay weight category."

In order to answer this, I had to work out how much weight he needed to lose and how long it would take him. From the chart I could see that he needed to lose about 20 kg.

My calculations show that it would take him about $13\frac{1}{3}$ weeks and that 4 months is about 18 weeks.

I would say that John's first statement isn't correct, as he should lose the weight in less time.

The second thing he says is, "If I go to the gym every morning and keep to my exercise plan, I will easily burn off the calories I ate at breakfast."

In order to answer this, I had to work out how many calories he ate for breakfast and how many calories he uses following his exercise plan.

My calculations show that he uses 440 calories, and that for breakfast he either eats 375 or 789 calories. So if he chooses the first breakfast he will burn off the calories he ate for breakfast, but if he chooses the second breakfast then he won't.

Helpful hints:

- **explain** what it is that you have worked out
- **explain** how your answers relate to the problem you've been asked to solve
- **compare** your answers to any statements in the problem
- draw **conclusions** based on the comparisons that you have made
- don't just write your answers with a 'Yes' or 'No' comment – a full explanation is needed!

Missed appointments

At a dental surgery, patients make an appointment to see either a dentist or a hygienist or both. If the patient misses their appointment they are fined according to the length of the appointment they missed. They are fined at the rate of £60 per hour.

At the end of 2007, the practice manager writes a report on the number of appointments that patients missed.

The practice manager writes,

"1. On average, more dentist appointments were missed per month than hygienist appointments.

2. Altogether the total money received from fines comes to £28 620."

Are the manager's statements correct?

Help 1

Surgery facts

The surgery opens from 9 am to 6 pm Monday to Friday.

The surgery closes for lunch from 1 pm to 2 pm.

There are six dentists at the surgery.

A dentist appointment lasts 15 minutes.

There are three hygienists at the surgery.

A hygienist appointment lasts 10 minutes.

The total number of hygienist appointments missed in 2007 is 1008.

The median monthly number of hygienist appointments missed in 2007 is 81.

The modal monthly number of hygienist appointments missed in 2007 is 96.

There are two receptionists at the surgery.

Help 3

Number of dentist and hygienist appointments missed in 2007

Bar chart titled "Number of dentist and hygienist appointments missed in 2007". Vertical axis: Number of appointments missed, from 70 to 110. Horizontal axis: Month (Jan–Dec). Legend: Dentist, Hygienist.

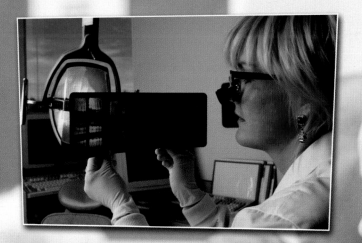

1 Find the number of dentist appointments missed each month in 2007.

Representing.

2 Calculate the averages (mean, median and mode) for the dentists' data.

Analysing.

3 Is the practice manager's first statement correct?

Interpreting.

4 Convert the total number of dentist and hygienist appointments missed into total time missed in hours.

Analysing.

5 Work out the total amount of money received from fines.

Analysing.

6 Is the practice manager's second statement correct?

Interpreting.

7 Make sure you show how and why you did each calculation at each stage.

Analysing.

8 Make sure you show that you have checked your calculations and considered the reasonableness of your answers.

Interpreting.

Help 2

Salary facts

A dentist at the surgery earns £86 000 per year.

A hygienist at the surgery earns £26 000 per year.

A receptionist at the surgery earns £15 000 per year.

It's my party and I'll cook if I want to

It's Greg's birthday, and he wants to have some fun.

He decides to throw a dinner party for himself, his wife and six close friends.

Here is the food he plans to serve.

Greg thinks he already has most of what he needs, and will only need to shop for seven new ingredients.

He allows himself about 3 hours to prepare and cook the meal.

Help Greg prepare his shopping list.

Does he only need seven new ingredients?

Has he given himself the right amount of time to make dinner?

What else should he add to the shopping list?

Menu

Stilton soup

~

Leek and macaroni bake

~

Rhubarb and orange crumble

Help 1

Greg's recipes

Stilton soup
(serves 4)

125 g	stilton cheese
50 g	butter
40 g	plain flour
900 ml	vegetable stock
300 ml	skimmed milk
60 ml	double cream
45 ml	white wine
1	onion

Cooking time: 45 mins
Preparation time: 25 mins

Leek and macaroni bake
(serves 6)

450 g	leeks
300 g	cheddar cheese
240 g	macaroni
75 g	butter
60 g	breadcrumbs
60 g	plain flour
900 ml	full-fat milk
30 g	chives

Cooking time: 45 mins
Preparation time: 20 mins
Oven temperature: 190°C

Rhubarb and orange crumble
(serves 10)

1.4 kg	rhubarb
225 g	butter
150 g	caster sugar
150 g	self-raising flour
150 g	plain flour
125 g	granulated sugar
2	eggs
1	orange

Cooking time: 1 hour
Preparationtime: 30 mins
Oven temperature: 200°C

1 Find the total amount that Greg needs of each ingredient.

Representing.

2 Work out the quantities of the ingredients that Greg needs to buy.

Analysing.

3 Write out Greg's shopping list.

Interpreting.

4 Is Greg correct about how many new ingredients he needs?

Interpreting.

5 Find the preparation and cooking times of each dish.

Representing.

6 Work out the total time that Greg should take to prepare and cook the meal.

Analysing.

7 Has Greg allowed himself the right amount of time to prepare and cook the meal?

Interpreting.

8 Make sure you show how and why you did each calculation at each stage, and make sure you show that you have checked your calculations.

Analysing.

9 What other things do you think he needs to buy to go with the meal?

Interpreting.

Help 2

Some useful cooking hints!

- Soup can be prepared in advance and re-heated before serving.
- One vegetable stock cube will make 200 ml of vegetable stock.
- Leek and macaroni bake must be served straight from the oven.
- Organic leeks have a better flavour than normal leeks.
- Make your own breadcrumbs from slices of white bread.
- Tinned rhubarb can be used instead of fresh rhubarb.
- For an extra-sweet finish, sprinkle icing sugar on top of the crumble.

Help 3

In his kitchen, Greg already has:

250 g	butter
1 kg	plain flour
1 kg	self-raising flour
1 l	skimmed milk
1 l	full-fat milk
250 ml	single cream
250 ml	double cream
500 g	spaghetti
400 g	cheddar cheese
$\frac{1}{2}$ dozen	eggs
8	vegetable stock cubes
500 g	granulated sugar
$\frac{1}{2}$ bottle	red wine
$\frac{1}{2}$ loaf	white bread
1	onion
3	oranges

Main courses for horses

Penny owns 10 horses.

She believes it costs over £80 a week to feed them.

Is Penny correct?

Help 1

Penny's horses

Name	Height (hands high)	Age (years)	Work-load
Summer	16	8	Medium
Dolly	15	18	Light
Ruby	14.1	12	Hard
Mr Bean	15.1	14	Medium
Kipper	14.3	13	Hard
Ladybird	16	12	Hard
Barney	14.2	8	Light
Maggie	15.2	9	Light
Jake	15.3	11	Hard
Fudge	15	15	Medium

Help 2

Food and drink for horses

The **amount** of food a horse needs each day depends on the height of the horse.

The **type** of food given to a horse depends on how hard it has to work.

Horses are fed a mixture of **hay** and a **hard feed** such as oats.

Penny doesn't have to buy hay, she produces her own.

On average a horse drinks 35 litres of water a day.

A 20 kg sack of hard feed costs £6.

Horses like treats such as apples and carrots.

Feed chart

Height of horse (cm)	140	142.5	145	147.5	150	152.5	155	157.5	160
Total daily weight of feed (kg)	10	10.2	10.5	10.8	11	11.2	11.5	11.7	12

Work it out!

1 Work out the height of each horse in centimetres.
Representing.

2 Work out the total daily weight of feed for each horse.
Analysing.

Help 5

Ratio of hay : hard feed

Work-load	Hay : hard feed
Light	4 : 1
Medium	7 : 3
Hard	2 : 1

3 Work out the daily weight of hard feed for each horse.
Representing.

4 Work out the total weekly weight of hard feed.
Analysing.

Help 3

Measuring horses

A horse is measured in hands and inches.

There are four inches in one hand.

A 15.3 hh horse measures 15 hands and 3 inches.

To convert hands and inches into centimetres, use this formula

$$C = 2.5(4H + I)$$

where C is the number of centimetres

H is the number of hands

I is the number of inches.

5 Work out the weekly cost.
Analysing.

6 Make sure you show and check your calculations.
Are your results sensible?
Analysing.

7 Compare your answer with Penny's.
Interpreting.

Roof gardens

Bryn moves into a small flat in Cardiff. The flat has a roof garden.

Bryn makes a scale drawing of the new design for his roof garden.

The garden will have wooden fencing on three sides.

There will be five large plant pots, each 1 m high.

Bryn wants the sides of the pots to be covered with bamboo.

Each pot will be filled with compost, leaving a 10 cm gap at the top.

Bryn says, *"The total cost of the pots, bamboo, compost and fencing is just under £1200."*

Is Bryn correct?

Help 1

Scale drawing of roof garden

Scale

1 : 100

Key

⎯ Fence   ▢ Plant pots

Haroldston garden centre price list

Plant pots (1 m high):		
square 1 m × 1 m	£49	
square 1.2 m × 1.2 m	£59	
square 1.4 m × 1.4 m	£69	
rectangular 1 m × 2 m	£49	
rectangular 1 m × 2.5 m	£69	
rectangular 1.2 m × 2.5 m	£89	
circular pot, radius 1 m	£99	
circular pot, radius 1.1 m	£119	
circular pot, radius 1.2 m	£139	
Fencing:	wooden	£9	per metre
	wire	£7	per metre
Bamboo:	roll (0.5 m high)	£3.50	per metre
	roll (1 m high)	£5.50	per metre
	roll (1.5 m high)	£7.50	per metre
Compost:	200 litre bag	£8.95	

Useful information

The perimeter of a circle = $2\pi r$
The area of a circle = πr^2
The volume of a cylinder = $\pi r^2 h$
The perimeter of a rectangle = $2(l + w)$
The area of a rectangle = lw
The volume of a cuboid = lwh
1 cm³ = 1 ml
1000 ml = 1 litre
1000 litres = 1 m³

Roll of bamboo covering

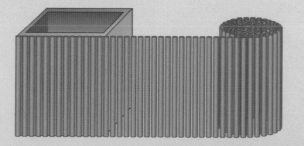

Work it out!

1 Use the scale drawing to work out the dimensions of the roof garden and plant pots.
Representing.

2 Work out the length of fencing for the garden and the cost of this fencing.
Analysing.

3 Work out the perimeter of each plant pot and the cost of the bamboo to clad these pots.
Analysing.

4 Work out the volume of compost needed for each pot and the cost of this compost.
Analysing.

5 Find the cost of the five plant pots.
Representing.

6 Work out the total cost of the pots, bamboo, compost and fencing.
Analysing.

7 Make sure you show and check your calculations. Are your results sensible?
Analysing.

8 Compare your answer with Bryn's. Is he correct?
Interpreting.

To market, to market

Gordon is a sheep farmer in England.

When he sells his lambs at market, he keeps careful records.

Looking at his records, Gordon says:

"Each week, I earn more per kilogram of meat than the average for England.

The mean live weight of my lambs was over 35 kg per lamb, and the weights were most varied the week of the 29 May.

My lambs were in very good condition four out of the five weeks that I sent them to the market."

Is each of Gordon's statements right?

Help 1

Gordon's records

Date	Number of lambs sent to market	Total live weight (kg)	Range of live weights (kg)	Total weight of meat (kg)	Total price paid for the meat (£)
1 May	14	504	4.5	220	457.60
8 May	9	315	3	130	257.40
15 May	10	340	5	146	268.64
22 May	22	792	6.5	340	652.80
29 May	17	646	7	245	465.50

Lamb facts

The total number of lambs in the UK in 2007 was 16 855 000.

An adult sheep's fleece weighs about 6 kg.

A male sheep is called a ram and a female sheep is called a ewe.

A lamb goes to market when it is between $2\frac{1}{2}$ and 3 months old.

The lambs are said to be in 'very good condition' if the total weight of meat is over 40% of the total live weight.

A sheep will eat 4% of its bodyweight in feed each day.

Start by working out the price per kg that Gordon was paid each week.

To find the weekly mean live weight divide the total live weight by the number of lambs.

What are ewe waiting for? Have a go at the Level 1 'Spring lambs' first as there's no range or percentages to do. Chop-chop, ewe need to finish Level 2 as well!

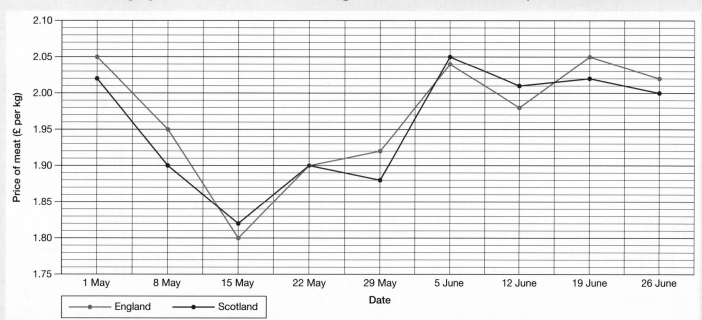

Average price of lamb meat in England and Scotland, May–June 2008

Setting up shop

Bob and Alexandria want to set up a new flower shop business in France. They need to find a suitable premises in which to open their shop.

This is their wish list.

> The shop must be
> - no more than 75 miles from Toulouse airport
> - no more than 60 miles from the sea
> - less than £145 000.
>
> The shop must have at least 2 storage areas.
> It must have easy local parking.
> It must have at least two floors.

Which of the shops meet all of the requirements on their 'wish list'?

Which shop would you advise them to buy and why?

Help 1

Help 2

Map information

There are airports at Toulouse, Castres, Beziers and Carcasonne.

Toulouse airport is to the west of Toulouse.

The A61-E80 is the motorway from Toulouse to Narbonne.

The N113 is the main road from Toulouse to Narbonne.

The map has a scale of 1 : 1 000 000

Resource sheet 1 provides a simplified version of the map to work from.

Shops for sale

Town	Number of storerooms	Number of bathrooms	Easy parking nearby	Security cameras fitted	Number of floors	Price (euros)
Limoux	1	1	✗	✗	1	140 000
Lagrasse	2	1	✓	✓	2	180 000
Bédarieux	2	2	✗	✗	3	178 000
Montréal	3	2	✓	✓	2	205 000
Béziers	2	1	✗	✓	1	215 000
Chalabre	1	1	✓	✗	2	168 000
Mazamet	3	1	✗	✓	1	190 000
Pézenas	2	2	✗	✓	3	184 000
Alzonne	2	2	✓	✗	2	172 000
Lacaune	2	1	✓	✗	2	164 000

Help 3

Currency exchange rates

Although it varies from day to day, on this occasion £1 can be exchanged for:

American	$ 1.87	Hong Kong	$ 14.53
Australian	$ 1.94	Singapore	$ 2.50
Canadian	$ 1.85	New Zealand	$ 2.36
Euro	€ 1.25	Japanese	Yen 193

Help 4

Some handy conversions

A kilogram is a bit more than 2 pounds

A pound is approximately 450 grams

A litre is less than 2 pints

A gallon is about 4.5 litres

A metre is a bit more than a yard

5 miles is about 8 km

A foot is about 30 cm

Hint 1

Work out the **maximum** price that Bob and Alexandria can spend in **euros**.

Hint 2

Find the shops that have **at least** two storerooms, **have** easy local parking, **have** at least two floors, and are **less** than Bob and Alexandria's maximum price.

Too hard?

Do the Level 1 'Moving back to France' first. Although it looks similar, it is not as hard, but you will still need your compass and ruler!

Beachcombers

Ros takes part in a UK beach litter survey every year.

She uses the results of the survey to compare the types of litter found on the beaches in England, Scotland, Wales and Northern Ireland.

Ros says,

"In 2007, there were more items of litter from beach visitors in Northern Ireland than from sewage in Scotland.
The mean number of items of litter per volunteer, in 2007, was highest in England.
Northern Ireland had the highest range in items of litter per kilometre from 2003 to 2006."

Are Ros's statements correct? Explain your answers.

Help 1

Beach litter survey details for 2007

Country	Number of beaches surveyed	Total number of volunteers	Total number of items of litter	Total length of beach surveyed (km)
Northern Ireland	4	50	4395	4
Scotland	44	520	39120	22
Wales	39	515	45132	17
England	208	2310	215082	109

Help 2

Useful information for 2007

The beach litter survey took place on 10 and 11 October.

303729 items of litter were collected from the beaches in the UK.

3543 bags were used.

The volunteers took over 7600 hours to collect all the litter.

Over 50% of all the litter collected was plastic.

Help 3

Items of litter per kilometre found on the beaches from 2003 to 2006

	Items/km in 2003	Items/km in 2004	Items/km in 2005	Items/km in 2006
Northern Ireland	482	1889	625	1063
Scotland	1526	1765	2089	2734
Wales	2588	1749	2534	2658
England	2262	2258	1988	2017

Types of litter found on the beaches in 2007

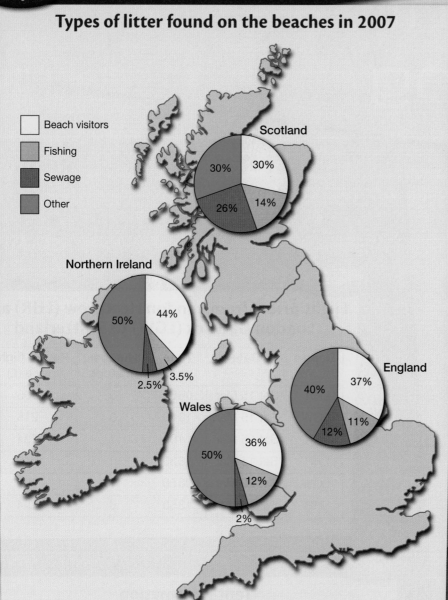

Beach visitors
Fishing
Sewage
Other

Scotland
30% 30%
30% 14%
26%

Northern Ireland
50% 44%
2.5% 3.5%

England
40% 37%
12% 11%

Wales
50% 36%
12%
2%

Hint 1

Make sure that you use the pie charts to compare the **percentage of litter** in **Northern Ireland** that came from **beach visitors**, and the **percentage of litter** in **Scotland** that came from **sewage**.

Hint 2

Make sure that you know how to work out the **mean** and the **range**, you are not asked for the mode or the median.

Too hard?

Drop down to the Level 1 'Litter bugs!' task and pick up some practice with the mean and pie charts.

Starlight trekking

To try and raise money for charity, Miguel has decided to take part in a sponsored trek for a week across the mountains of Switzerland.

He books the afternoon non-stop flight from London (Heathrow) on Saturday 15 March.

The flight returns on Saturday 22 March.

Miguel plans to purchase...

▶ the lightest, tallest tent he can find – the internal height must be over 1m

▶ the cheapest sleeping bag that gives him enough protection from the cold at night

▶ £125 of euros.

Miguel has already ordered his lightweight food packs, which will cost him £76.

Miguel says, *"If I round all the prices to the nearest £10, I estimate the total costs of the camping trip is going to be £550."*

Is Miguel correct?

Help 1

Flight prices from London Heathrow (LHR) and London Gatwick (LGW) to Switzerland

Depart	Date	Time	Number of stops	Return flight price (£)
LHR	Sat 15 Mar	06 50	0	195
LGW	Sat 15 Mar	13 40	0	215
LHR	Sat 15 Mar	14 00	1	234
LHR	Sat 15 Mar	18 30	0	242
LGW	Sat 22 Mar	08 50	1	199
LHR	Sat 22 Mar	13 50	0	224

Help 2

Tent information

Name of tent	Weight (kg)	Pack dimensions (cm) length × width	Internal height (cm)	Colour	Price (£)
Trekker	2.4	48 × 20	120	Green	199.99
Sport	2.8	53 × 27	95	Red	29.99
Getup	2.05	51 × 14	110	Green	39.99
Shadow	3.15	46 × 32	115	Blue	59.99
Beta	2.35	49 × 12	95	Brown	79.99

Hint 1

Make sure that you ignore the information in the tables that you don't need.

Hint 2

Be careful when rounding off the amounts that you need.

Too hard?

Why not try the Level 1 'Camping with wolves' task first; it will help you develop the skills necessary to complete this task.

Help 3

Sleeping bag information

Name of sleeping bag	Lowest temperature (°C)	Pack dimensions (cm) length × width	Price (£)	Customer rating
Arctic square	−12	37 × 24	54.99	★
Nordic	−4	36 × 19	19.99	★★★★
Greenland	−10	45 × 23	84.99	★★★
Ultralight	0	44 × 22	16.99	★★★★
Warm 'n' cosy	−5	28 × 17	32.99	★★★★★
Deep down	−24	42 × 20	99.99	★★

Help 4

Night-time temperatures in the mountains

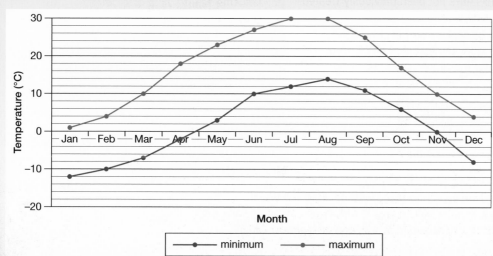

Decking

Kyle is putting new decking in his garden.

The decking is made from planks of wood 2 m long and 12 cm wide.

This is a sketch of the decking area (not drawn to scale).

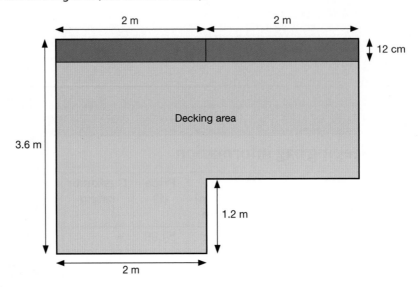

(a) How many planks of wood does Kyle need for the decking?

You must show your calculations and state how you used them to get your answer.

DECKING INFORMATION

- The weight of a 1 m × 0.1 m plank is 2.7 kg.
- It should take about 3 minutes to fix each plank in place.
- The planks have not been previously treated with decking oil.
- One litre of decking oil will cover 6 m² of decking for the first coat and 8 m² of decking for the second coat.
- Remember to oil the decking once a year.
- The formula to work out the number of screws for the decking is:

  $S = 6p$ where: S is the number of screws
  p is the number of planks

PRICE LIST

Decking screws (pack of 200)	£7.18
Decking planks (1 m × 0.1 m)	£4.50 each
Decking planks (1 m × 0.12 m)	£4.80 each
Decking planks (1 m × 0.15 m)	£4.95 each
Decking planks (2 m × 0.1 m)	£5.00 each
Decking planks (2 m × 0.12 m)	£5.25 each
Decking planks (2 m × 0.15 m)	£5.75 each

Special offer – buy one get one half price!

Decking oil (1 litre can)	£6.50
Wood preservative (10 litre can)	£46.50

The planks of wood are fixed into place with decking screws.
Once the decking is in place, Kyle paints it with two coats of decking oil.
Kyle says, *"The total cost of the wood, screws and oil is almost £300."*

(b) Is Kyle correct?

You must show your calculations and state how you used them to get your answer.

You're the examiner!

Look through the following answers written by a student.

See if you can allocate the examiner's comments to the correct parts of the student's answers.

(a)

First of all I need to divide the decking area into two rectangles and then work out the number of planks needed for each rectangle.

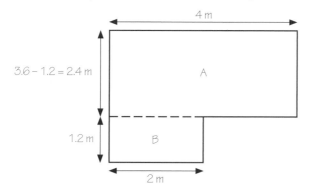

A Each plank is 12 cm wide (12 cm = 0.12 m) and 2 m long

Rectangle A: $2.4 \div 0.12 = 20$ and $4 \div 2 = 2$
       number of planks $= 20 \times 2 = 40$

Rectangle B: $1.2 \div 0.12 = 10$ and $2 \div 2 = 1$
       number of planks $= 10 \times 1 = 10$

Total number of planks $= 40 + 10 = 50$

(b)

B First of all I need to work out the cost of the planks. Then I need to work out how many screws Kyle needs and the cost of these screws. Finally I need to work out the area of the decking, so I can work out how much oil is needed and then find the cost of this oil.

Cost of planks $= 50 \times £5.25 = \underline{£262.50}$ Check: $50 \times 5 = 250$ ✓

C Number of screws $= 6 \times 50 = 300$, so Kyle needs to buy 2 packets
Cost of screws $= 2 \times £7.18 = \underline{£14.36}$ Check: $2 \times 7 = 14$ ✓

D Area of decking: Rectangle A $4 \times 2.4 = 9.6 \text{ m}^2$
          Rectangle B $2 \times 1.2 = 2.4 \text{ m}^2$
          Total area $9.6 + 2.4 = 12 \text{ m}^2$
1st coat of oil $12 \div 6 = 2$ litres
2nd coat of oil $12 \div 8 = 1.5$ litres

E Total amount of oil $2 + 1.5 = 3.5$ litres, so Kyle needs to buy 4 cans
Cost of oil $4 \text{ cans} \times £6.50 = £26$ Check: $4 \times 7 = 28$ ✓

Total cost $= £262.50 + £14.36 + £26 = \underline{£302.86}$
               Check: $260 + 10 + 30 = 300$ ✓

F Kyle is wrong, the total cost is just over £300.

1 **Examiner says...**
Correct use of the formula given.

2 **Examiner says...**
Incorrect interpretation of 'Special offer'.

3 **Examiner says...**
Correct conversion of cm into m.

4 **Examiner says...**
Student has interpreted their answers correctly.

5 **Examiner says...**
Very good plan.

6 **Examiner says...**
No checks shown.

Wood-burning stove

Dave's gas heating bill has risen dramatically in the last year, so he decides to buy a wood-burning stove to heat his lounge.

His lounge measures 4.9 m wide by 6.4 m long by 2.8 m high.

Dave knows that he has to buy a stove with a kilowatt rating higher than the kilowatts needed to heat his lounge.

Dave sees this formula on the internet:

$$\text{Kilowatts needed to heat a room} = \frac{\text{volume of room (m}^3)}{14}$$

(a) How many kilowatts are needed to heat Dave's lounge?
You must show your calculations and state how you used them to get your answer.

Dave looks at this brochure showing the details of some wood-burning stoves.

Stove model number	Height (inches)	Width (inches)	Depth (inches)	Weight (kg)	Kilowatt rating	Price (£)
A275	24	26	17	120	12	350
A330	22.5	26.5	15.5	98	9	375
J20	24.5	22.75	13.5	90	8	275
J55	23	17.5	13.5	68	6	225
F222	29	28	18.5	165	16	450
F285	23	19	12	78	5	275
F188	28	33.5	22	197	18	650
G390	24.5	18.5	15.5	74	7	350

Accessories

Tool set	£36.50	Log carrier	£75.99
Single screen	£64.89	Log basket	£16.99
Double screen	£96.50	Log tongs	£20.45
Hearth set	£14.99	Ash carrier	£63.99

Our top 4 sellers!

A275
G390
J55
J20

Cost of delivery on all orders: £35

Dave measures the place where the stove will go. The stove he buys must have less than these maximum dimensions: height of 65 cm, width of 60 cm and depth of 40 cm.

Dave orders a stove, single screen, log basket and hearth set.
He has a maximum budget of £500 for the stove, accessories and delivery.

(b) Which stove do you recommend that Dave buys?

You must show your calculations and state how you used them to get your answer.

Look through the following answers written by a student.

See if you can allocate the examiner's comments to the correct parts of the student's answers.

(a)

A
First of all I need to work out the volume of the room in cubic metres. Then I must use the formula to work out how many kilowatts are needed to heat Dave's lounge.

Volume = 4.9 × 6.4 × 2.8 = 87.808 m³   Check: 5 × 6 × 3 = 90 ✓
Kilowatts = 87.808 ÷ 14 = 6.272 kw   Check: 90 ÷ 15 = 6 ✓

(b)

B
First of all I need to work out the height, width and depth of all the stoves in cm. Then I can use the table to work out which ones fit in Dave's room. Then I need to work out the total cost of the accessories, so I can find the maximum that Dave can spend on his stove. Finally I need to decide which stove Dave should buy.

I know that Dave needs a stove that has a kilowatt rating of over 6.272 to heat his lounge, so I can ignore the J55 and the F285 models.

To convert inches to cm I multiply by 2.5

C

Model number	Height (cm)	Width (cm)	Depth (cm)
A275	60	65	42.5
A330	56.25	66.25	38.75
J20	61.25	56.875	33.75
F222	72.5	70	46.25
F188	70	83.75	55
G390	61.25	46.25	38.75

I can now see that the F222 and the F188 are too high, the A275, A330, F222 and F188 are too wide and the A275, the F222 and the F188 are too deep.

The J20 and G390 are possible stoves that would fit.

D
The accessories that Dave wants to buy cost £64.89, £75.99 and £14.99

E
The total cost of the accessories and delivery is:
    64.89 + 75.99 + 14.99 + 35 = £192.87

The maximum Dave can spend on the stove is: 500 − 192.87 = £307.13
                    Check: 500 − 200 = 300 ✓

F
The only stove that Dave can afford is the J20.

---

1 Examiner says...
Correct conversion of inches into cm.

2 Examiner says...
One incorrect price.

3 Examiner says...
Correct use of the formula given.

4 Examiner says...
Student has interpreted their answers correctly.

5 Examiner says...
Correct interpretation of 'kilowatt rating'.

6 Examiner says...
No check of total cost.

Diving dilemma

(a) Rodrigo is a very keen scuba diver, and regularly goes diving at the weekend. Each of Rodrigo's dives lasts about an hour. Rodrigo buys a scuba diving torch – it runs on four 'C cell' batteries. According to the manufacturer, the four batteries will power the torch for about two hours underwater.

Rodrigo has a choice between disposable or rechargeable batteries. He looks on the internet to investigate the cost of disposable and rechargeable batteries. Which of these is the better buy over a single dive season of eight months?

**Four pack disposable
C cell batteries
Price £6.10**

**Battery charger
Price: £19.99 + post and
packaging (£2.95)**

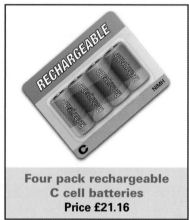

**Four pack rechargeable
C cell batteries
Price £21.16**

State clearly any assumptions you make.

[14 marks]

(b) Rodrigo also likes playing computer games. He uses a free games download site.

He always loads games on to his 4 gigabyte memory stick but he has only got 178 megabytes of available space left.

Which games can he load on to his memory stick to use up as much of the available space as possible?

Game	Size (MB)
Age de Castles	12
Alien Action	8
Air Stroke	26
Ant Attack	11
Aztec Blocks	15
Gosh	37
Locoo	12
Oasis	14
Orbizter	17

Game	Size (MB)
Qwind2	16
Reazzon	21
Seam	40
Swarm Of	13
Water Wild	14
Zed CarZ	11
7 Spots	9
7 Spots II	11

State clearly any assumptions you make.

[4 marks]

Johan is a part-time bus inspector. His records show the buses he inspects over a three-week period.

Bus Number	Time Due	Minutes Late	Day
X5	0735	6	Monday – 2 April
N19	0802	3	Monday – 2 April
N24	0924	17	Monday – 2 April
X5	0953	7	Monday – 2 April
D18	1520	1	Wednesday – 4 April
D31	1544	4	Wednesday – 4 April
D82	1607	11	Wednesday – 4 April
D50	1637	4	Wednesday – 4 April
D18	1715	10	Wednesday – 4 April
161	2030	12	Thursday – 5 April
A41	2057	7	Thursday – 5 April
232	2120	10	Thursday – 5 April
161	2205	18	Thursday – 5 April
GB007	1110	3	Saturday – 7 April
GB011	1130	3	Saturday – 7 April
LB36	1155	7	Saturday – 7 April
LB24	1217	5	Saturday – 7 April
LB36	1242	9	Saturday – 7 April
GB007	1300	14	Saturday – 7 April
FS1	1315	6	Monday – 9 April
FS2	1340	12	Monday – 9 April
FS6	1410	7	Monday – 9 April

Bus Number	Time Due	Minutes Late	Day
FS1	1450	9	Monday – 9 April
12	2235	6	Wednesday – 11 April
19	2247	4	Wednesday – 11 April
27	2312	2	Wednesday – 11 April
14	2330	7	Wednesday – 11 April
24	2350	5	Wednesday – 11 April
16	0010	1	Thursday – 12 April
12	0028	3	Thursday – 12 April
X5	0735	2	Friday – 13 April
N19	0802	9	Friday – 13 April
N24	0924	9	Friday – 13 April
X5	0953	6	Friday – 13 April
D18	1120	4	Monday – 16 April
D31	1144	10	Monday – 16 April
D82	1207	4	Monday – 16 April
D50	1237	3	Monday – 16 April
D18	1315	3	Monday – 16 April
FS1	0615	2	Wednesday – 18 April
FS2	0640	6	Wednesday – 18 April
FS8	0659	2	Wednesday – 18 April
FS7	0740	9	Wednesday – 18 April
FS1	0850	16	Wednesday – 18 April

Johan, in his monthly report says

• Buses tend to be at least 5 minutes late in the afternoon.

• The probability of a bus being late by at least 8 minutes is 50%.

• Buses on Mondays tend to be later than buses on Wednesdays.

Does the data in the table support these three statements?

State clearly any assumptions you make.

[18 marks]

Mr Muscle

'Muscle Shakes' is advertised as a new supplement to help bodybuilders to gain weight quickly. A newspaper asks a fitness and bodybuilding club to test whether this claim is true or not.

To carry out the test the club asked its 43 male members to take part. They were divided into four groups; A, B, C and D.

They were weighed before and after the experiment.
The results are shown in the 'Experiment results' tables.

The groups have the following different exercise programmes, calorie-controlled diet and food supplements.

- Group A – light weights, calorie-controlled diet and placebo milkshake
- Group B – light weights, calorie-controlled diet and Muscle Shakes milkshake
- Group C – heavy weights, calorie-controlled diet and placebo milkshake
- Group D – heavy weights, calorie-controlled diet and Muscle Shakes milkshake

Note: A placebo milkshake is an ordinary milkshake with no active ingredients. However, the men drinking the placebo milkshake will not know this and so they might believe it is a Muscle Shakes milkshake.

Experiment results

Group A – light weights, calorie-controlled diet and placebo milkshake

Member	Age (years)	Weight change (kg)
1	29	+9
2	23	+7.5
3	27	–3
4	24	+11
5	32	+1
6	40	+5.5
7	21	+2.5
8	26	+1.5
9	30	–4
10	27	+0.5

Group B – light weights, calorie-controlled diet and Muscle Shakes milkshake

Member	Age (years)	Weight change (kg)
11	21	–2
12	26	+5
13	30	+2
14	23	+6.5
15	25	+6
16	31	+9
17	22	+3.5
18	28	+5.5
19	29	–2.5
20	25	+0.5
21	29	+5

Group C – heavy weights, calorie-controlled diet and placebo milkshake

Member	Age (years)	Weight change (kg)
22	19	+10
23	28	+4.5
24	30	+3
25	22	+7.5
26	23	+9.5
27	27	+2.5
28	24	+1
29	26	+8.5
30	34	+3
31	27	+4

Group D – heavy weights, calorie-controlled diet and Muscle Shakes milkshake

Member	Age (years)	Weight change (kg)
32	25	+0.5
33	25	+1.5
34	25	+11.5
35	32	+2.5
36	19	+8.5
37	22	+2.5
38	27	+10.5
39	24	0
40	20	+10
41	27	+11
42	25	+1.5
43	24	0

Use the information in the tables to investigate the claim in the advert that 'Muscle Shakes' helps bodybuilders gain weight.

You must show your calculations and state how you have used them to get your answer.

[18 marks]

Potty about plants

A plant nursery has a stand at an exhibition. The nursery wants to put as many plants as possible in their stand. Because they are near a fire exit the stand is separated into two blocks.

There must be a 4 m wide gangway to the fire exit and a 3 m wide gangway along the wall. The exhibition staff are very strict on these rules as well as making sure that exhibitors keep within their boundaries.

Here is a rough sketch of the part of the hall where the plant nursery has a stand.

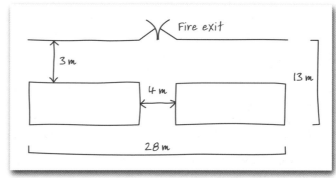

The plant nursery uses only one type of pot in their display. This diagram gives the measurements of a pot. There must be at least 1300 mm between rows of pots for people to walk down.

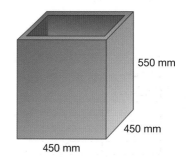

This picture shows how the plant pots have to be placed for the exhibition.

The pots are all on wheeled trolleys in a lorry. It takes about 9 minutes to push a trolley from the lorry and put the pots in rows. Each trolley carries six plant pots.

How long should it take 4 workers from the plant nursery to set out the pots for the exhibition?

You must show your calculations and state how you have used them to get your answer.   **[18 marks]**